THE ULTIMATE GNATRAT

THE ULTIMATE GNATRAT

BY MARK MARTIN

FRONT COVER BY ALLEN FREEMAN
AND MARK MARTIN

TYPESETTING BY BEN BURFORD

FANTAGRAPHICS BOOKS
7563 Lake City Way NE
Seattle WA 98115

Written, illustrated, edited, and produced by
MARK MARTIN

Fantagraphics Production Staff:
KIM THOMPSON and MARK THOMPSON

Separations by RAYSON FILMS
Special thanks to Joe at PORT PUBLICATIONS

Much of the material in this book was originally published in *The Dark Gnat Returns*, *Happy Birthday Gnatrat*, and *Darerat/Tadpole: Prankster*, respectively published by Prelude Graphics, Dimension Graphics, and Mighty Pumpkin; lots of pages in *The Ultimate Gnatrat* are brand new, however, and make it well worth buying even if you have all the grubby old comic books.

First Fantagraphics Books edition: April 1990

1 3 5 7 9 8 6 4 2

ISBN: 1-56097-027-8

Printed by Port Publications of Port Washington, WI

I'm about to DIE and my LIFE suddenly spins before me!

MAYBE THIS TIME IT'LL MAKE SENSE

NOTHING IS REAL!!

IS IT NOW? OR THEN

MILLISECONDS ARE DECADES!
EONS ARE ETERNITIES!
LIGHTBULBS ARE HEADBANDS!

I'M IN A CAR!
A RACE CAR!

TA HAND IT TO WHO-
R LAID THIS ONE OUT.
RIDING A **SNAKE**!

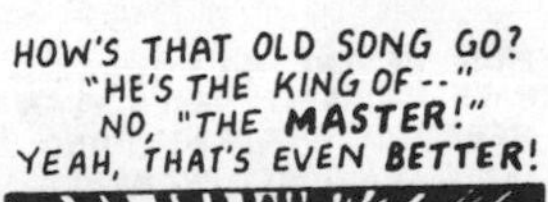
HOW'S THAT OLD SONG GO?
"HE'S THE KING OF--"
NO, "THE **MASTER**!"
YEAH, THAT'S EVEN **BETTER**!

BOO

HE'S THE MASTER OF
GOOOOOOOOOING
FAAAAAAAASTER!

THAT'S ME ALL OVER!
MASTER BOO!
GOING FASTER...

FASTER!
FASTER!!

FAS--:: A CURVE!
TOO SHARP!!

THIS WOULD BE A **FINE**
DEATH...

THIS **WOULD** BE A FINE
DEATH...
GAME OVER

I HADN'T RUN OUT OF
TOKENS!
PULL
PREPARE
TO
QUALIF
ON

I COULD BUY MORE TOKENS.
ALL THE TOKENS. HELL, I
COULD BUY THE WHOLE
BLOOMIN' **ARCADE**! THE
WHOLE FOREST!
STEP ON A
KRAK

AFTER ALL, I **AM**
GAZILLIONAIRE PLAYRAT
BOO SWAIN!
PAC RAT

NO. IT'S BETTER THIS WAY.
EXIT
CEREAL
KILLER

PAINTED EVERY SEWER CAP
IN THE FOREST LIKE A
HIDEOUS YELLOW
HAPPY FACE!

THIS IS JUST THE **LATEST**
IN A **SERIES** OF **VILE**
CRIMES PERPETRATED BY
YOUTHFUL ART GANGS
IN THE FOREST!

-- OVER TO YOU, WALLY--
WHAT'S OUR WEATHER
SITUATION?

HOT, LIZ.
HOT

-- ALSO IN THE NEWS -- TODAY MARKS THE FIFTIETH ANNIVERSARY OF THE LAST REPORTED SIGHTING OF THE GNATRAT!
THIS WOULD MAKE THE OLD BOY AT LEAST 90 YEARS OLD -- IF HE'S STILL ALIVE, WHICH I DOUBT.
MOST OF THE KIDS TODAY HAVE PROBABLY NEVER EVEN HEARD OF GNATRAT... AND THE OLDER GOATS PROBABLY COULDN'T CARE LESS! IN FACT, I DON'T KNOW WHY WE EVEN BOTHERED TO MENTION THIS!
?
IT'S BETTER THIS WAY.
BETTER TO LEAVE IT ALL BEHIND ME. DON'T THINK ABOUT THE GOOD OLD DA BEFORE THE ART GANGS. BEFORE WE RAN OUT OF GAS.
BETTER TO BE THANKFUL WE STILL HAVE ELECTRICI AT LEAST! WHAT WOULD USE TO CARRY THIS STOR IF NOT CUTAWAYS TO TELEVISION SCREENS!
YEAH, WE STILL HAVE ELECTRICITY, THANK NIM BUT NO GAS ... WE WERE SUPPOSED TO BE TRIPPING ALL OVER THE UNIVERSE BY NOW, ACCORDING TO THE OLD COMIC BOOKS!
INSIDE
MUTANT MONTHLY
TEEN TERROR
SLICE N DICE
GOT A PENNY LEAVE A PENNY NEED A PENNY DROP DEAD
DAMNED NEWS & BOOKS
SHOP AT DAMNED
-- THIS JUST IN -- A CUTE LITTLE BABY DU HAS JUST BEEN FOUND STAPLED TO THE FOREHE OF POLICE COMMISSIONE GONZO...
THE COMIC BOOKS!

IT WASN'T SO BAD AT FIRST... THAT FIRST SPIN-OFF WAS PRETTY GOOD, ACTUALLY...

PUBESCENT SPAZMO KUNG-FU TORTOISES

WH' HUH?

THEN CAME ANOTHER.

AND ANOTHER! AND ANOTHER! PARODIES OF PARODIES OF...

YOUNG SEX-MANIAC SUMO HOMOS

THIS ISSUE: WHO LEFT THE *G!!#* DOOR OPEN?

NOW LOOK AT 'EM!

PIMPLY FACED SECRET WARRIORS

TOILET TRAINED TINY TOTS

UNBORN HYBRID

JUMBO JEW JITSU JUNKIES

UPCHUC CHARLIE: CHUN KING CHOREBOYS

OOD RIDDANCE BAD ARBAGE!
YOU SAID IT, PAL!
HAVE YOU HEARD? THEY'RE GONNA GIVE MY JOB TO A WOMAN!

DAMN SHAME, JIM... IT'S NOT BECAUSE OF THAT BABY DUCK INCIDENT, IS IT?

FOR CRYIN' OUT LOUD, BOO! NOT YOU TOO! YOU NAME ME ONE POLITICAL FIGURE WHO HASN'T HAD A KINKY SEX ENCOUNTER WITH A PROSTITUTE OR A PAGE-BOY!

THEY ALL DO IT... AND THEY ALL GET CAUGHT!

THE MEDIA JUST DOESN'T HAVE ANYTHING BETTER TO TALK ABOUT RIGHT NOW! ALL THEY TALK ABOUT IS "HOT WEATHER THIS -- HOT WEATHER THAT!" IT'S NO WONDER THEY'RE CRUCIFYING ME!!

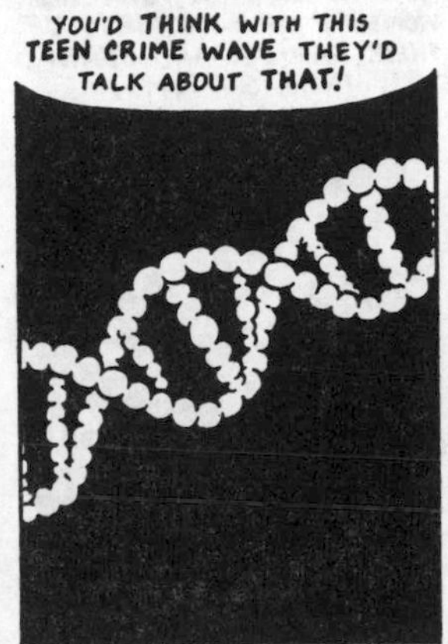
YOU'D THINK WITH THIS TEEN CRIME WAVE THEY'D TALK ABOUT THAT!
AND YOU! YOU'RE ONE TO TALK! ALWAYS MAKING LIKE YOU'RE DRINKING GINGER ALE, AND EVERYONE KNOWS YOU'RE PICKLED ON CHEAP WINE!

WELL, WHAT DO YOU HAVE TO SAY TO THAT, OLD FRIEND?

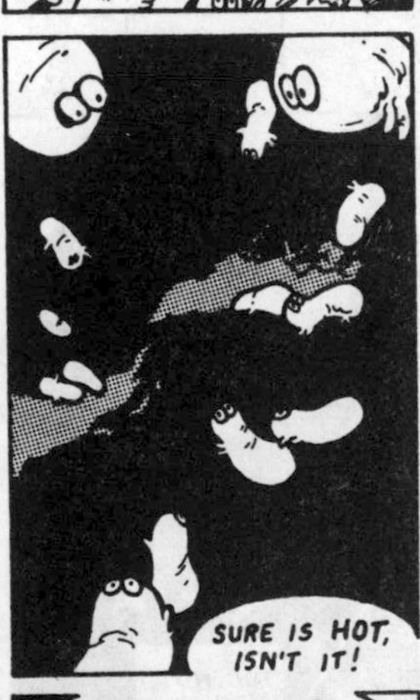
SURE IS HOT, ISN'T IT!

OUCH! DAMN GNATS!

I MEAN... IF IT'S SO HOT, WHY ARE WE WEARING THESE HUGE OVERCOATS??

LET'S FACE IT, BOO -- WE'RE GETTING OLD... SENILE. WE CAN'T DRESS SENSIBLY OR CARRY ON AN INTELLIGENT CONVERSATION.

BUT WE FOUGHT THE GOOD FIGHT, EH?

THESE GNATS ARE DRIVING ME BATS!

OH MAN, IT'S HOT!! I CAN'T REMEMBER WHEN I'VE EVER SEEN--

WE INTERRUPT FOR A SPECIAL NEWS BULLETIN-- WE'VE JUST RECIEVED A VIDEO-TAPED COMMUNIQUE FROM THE SELF-PROCLAIMED LEADER OF THE ART GANGS!

DO NOT CALL US ART GANGS.

WHEN OUR MENTORS WER OVERTHROWING YOUR PUNY COMIC BOOK INDUSTRY YOU COULD CALL US THAT.

NOW WE CONTROL MORE THAN JUST YOUR COMICS... WE CONTROL THE FOREST! NOW WE ARE THE LAW!

NOW WE WILL CAPTURE YOUR WOMEN -- WE WILL MESS UP THEIR HAIR-DOS AND SPANK THEIR BOTTOMS!

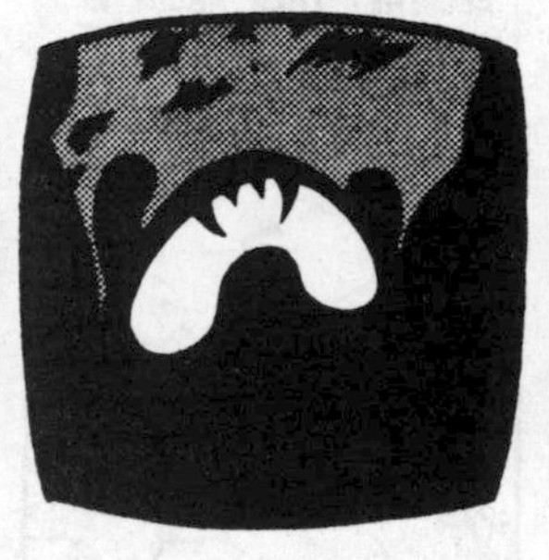

NOW WE WILL ENTER YOUR HOMES AT NIGHT AND RIP THE LABELS FROM YOUR CANNED GOODS!

AND I WILL HANG GONZO' HEAD FROM THE HIGHEST LIMB OF THE HIGHEST TREE IN THE FOREST.

BUT FIRST, A WORD FROM MY SPON--::
RGER
KINGPIN

THE REMAINDER OF THE TAPE IS TOO MORONIC TO BE BROADCAST HERE. WE NOW REJOIN OUR WEATHER FORECAST IN PROGRESS...

IT'S HOT.
TOO HOT.

AND WHEN IT'S HOT...

IT'S GNATTY.

AND WHEN IT'S GNATTY...

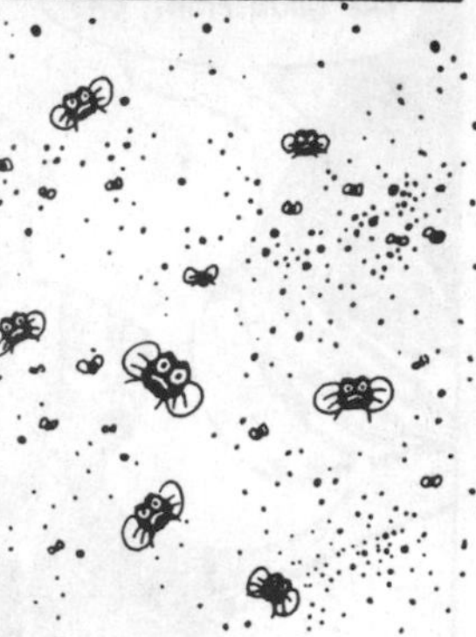

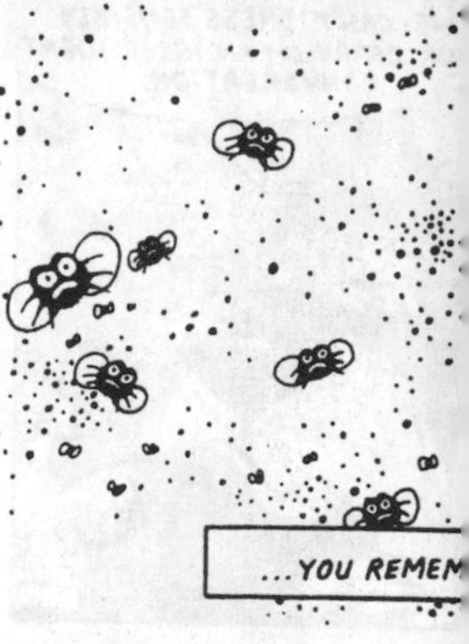

...YOU REMEM

U REMEMBER ANOTHER HOT, GNATTY NIGHT...
... A WITTLE BABY WAT ...
BUS STO
...A MOMMY RAT... A DADDY...
THE CHEF'S NOT A GOOD BOY-AR-
THE BULL'S OUT OF PLUMS
... ARTWORK ...
.. A CHILDREN'S COMIC ...
... BAD MANS ...
... ALL HE WANTED WAS TO CONTROL THE COMICS MARKET..
...THE WHOLE COMIC BOOK BUSINESS WAS GOING ALL TO HELL ...
...TRAIL OF DEAD MICE THREE MILES...
...WOMEN WITH MUSSED HAIR AND ROSY RED BOTTOMS...
KLIK
... KIDNAPPED CHILDREN OF CHICKEN LITTLE...
KLIK
... WITH A KNIFE IN HIS BLOOD-STAINED...
KLIK
... COW MUTILATION...

DAMMIT!
I JUST PAID FIFTY BUCKS TO GET THAT REMOTE FIXED!

...COLD AND EMPTY! ...EMPTY AS A THUNDERBIRD BOTTLE ON A PARK BENCH.
...COLD. IT'S ALWAYS COLD IN HERE -- IN HERE WHERE I THINK OF TADPOLE.
I THINK OF TADPOLE AND I WONDER...
...WHY THE HELL AM I STANDING HERE NAKED ?

Comics in your Future

ANARCHY

Twisted Sister's Festered Blisters (May) $1.95.

Fetal Boznoid Mai-Tai Flies 4: by Man

GET A GRIP ON THE DOOBIE, MAN! YOU ALMOST BURNED THAT KID!
... FAR OUT...

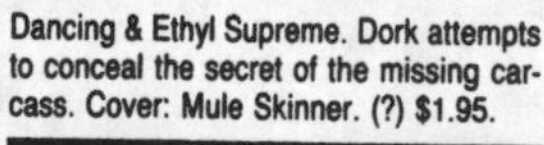

Dancing & Ethyl Supreme. Dork attempts to conceal the secret of the missing carcass. Cover: Mule Skinner. (?) $1.95.

BELLIGERENT

Umbilical Hairy Hari-Kari Hares 4: Mom discovers the boys trying to hang themselves with their cords. (May) $1.95.

Samurai Zygote 4: (May not) $1.95.

DYNAMIC FAILURES

Conceptual Screwed-Up Shaolin Whales 4: by Campiti & Jones. The whales go shopping for high heels. (May) $1.95.

Samurai Cow 4: (?) $1.95.

Post-Mortem Jack-Hammer Johnnies 4: Held captive by Liq'qid Plumm'r, the

HE COMIC-BUYING PUBLIC
'SERVES MORE THAN AN
NDLESS **SUCCESSION** OF
UTATED MARTIAL ARTS
ROUPS! WE DEMAND **VARIETY**
AND **QUALITY ARTWORK!**

BULLHOCKEY, LASAGNA!
THE PUBLIC GETS WHAT THE
PUBLIC **WANTS** -- IF YOUR
PRECIOUS **PUBLIC** DOESN'T
LIKE THE CURRENT FARE,
WHY DO THEY CONTINUE TO
BUY IT ?!!

IT'S NOT A **QUESTION** OF
SUPPLY AND DEMAND! IT'S
A SIMPLE CASE OF
MONOPOLY! THERE **IS** NO
ALTERNATIVE FARE BECAUSE
ART GANGS FORCIBLY --

PBBLLLLLLBBT!

HMPH!
THAT'S EXACTLY THE
ESPONSE I'D **EXPECT** FROM
SHREW OF YOUR **OBVIOUS**
MORAL FIBER!

ROTATE,
FATASS.

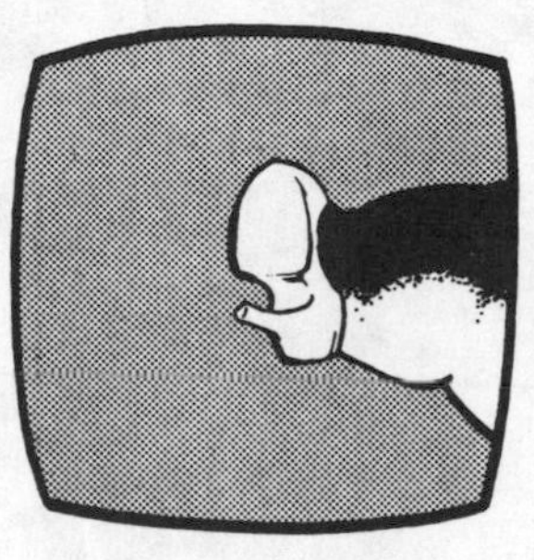

Monday
DING!

ORRY, RORY, BUT YOU'RE
T OF TIME -- PERMANENTLY!
OR THOSE OF YOU WHO
RE JUST NOW JOINING US,
DAY'S 'OH YEAH? - YEAH!'...

OH YEAH?
-YEAH!

CONCERNS THE COMIC BOOK
INDUSTRY. **DOES** FANDOM
WANT MORE VARIETY?
IF SO, **CAN** THEY GET IT?

APPROVED
BY THE
ART
GANG
AUTHORITY

... REACHED FOR COMMENT,
COMMISSIONER GONZO OFFERED
NONE ... **I** SAY HE'S POUT-
ING BECAUSE THEY GAVE HIS
JOB TO A **WOMAN!!** HA HA--

OOKS LIKE **YOU'RE** OUT OF
IME, TOO, SLIM -- LET'S
WITCH TO WEATHER
ADAR, AS I BELIEVE WE
AVE A **STORM** BREWING...

RIGHT, LIZ, AND IT'S
HEADING STRAIGHT FOR THE
FOREST, LIKE THE **FURY**
OF A **WOMAN SCOR**--

storm
forest

er... uh...
... that is...

BEEP
BUNNY, BOO. HOW'D YA LIKE YER WOUNDS LICKED?
KLIK

BEEP
BOO? KLARC. DIDJA GET YOUR PIZZAS? HA HA
KLIK
?

BEEP
MR. SWAIN, I'M CALLING TO CONFIRM YOUR ORDER FOR FIVE CHEESE PIZZAS WITH EXTRA EXTRA CHEESE.
KLIK

KRAK

ONE DOWN, CHICKEN LITTLE. IF YOU EVER WANT TO SEE WHAT'S LEFT OF THIS CARTON OF EGGS AGAIN, YOU'LL FIND A WAY TO COME UP--

JUST A SECOND MRS. LITTLE.. COME IN!!
KNOK
TAP

AS I WAS... COULD YOU EXCUSE ME AGAIN PLEASE!
WUMP!

HEY! HOLD IT DOWN OVER THERE! I'M ON THE PHONE!!

KKSSH!
PLAT!
SPLAT!
SPLAT! SPLAT!
SPLAT!
SPLAT!
SPLAT!
SPLAT!
SPLAT! SPLAT! SPLAT!
HEY, MAN, WHAT'S THE BIG IDEA? YOU MADE ME BREAK ALL THE EGGS!
..UH..
YOU STUPID JERK! I'M GOING TO GET THE MANAGER!
..YOU CAN TELL ALL YOUR LITTLE BUDDIES THERE'S MORE WHERE THAT CAME FROM!

--ALL UNITS-- HOODLUMS JUST USED SLUGS TO GET SOFT DRINKS FROM A MACHINE! --ALL UNITS--

'DUH...
OL' GONZO'LL STAPLE US TO HIS FOREHEAD IF WE LOSE THEM!

UH...I THINK I SEE SOME-BODY ELSE UP THERE.
DON'T TRY TO THINK, KID... YOU'LL HURT YOURSELF!

ARE YOU SLOWING DOWN?
NAAAH-- THE WORLD'S SPEEDING UP!

LOOK, KID-- YOU'RE YOUNG... A ROOKIE! YOU STILL GOT A LOT TO LEARN

?
YOU REACH A POINT WHEN ALL THIS RUNNING STARTS TO AFFECT YOU!
PD

NAIL
CHUCK
ASA
HAW! HAW! I KNEW THE OLD ONE WOULD GIVE OUT!
GNN-

WHIIIIIIPP!
RRRRRRRRRR!!!!
KUUNCH
OH MY GOD
OH MY GOD
OH MY GOD
CHUCK'S HEAD!
ASA
LEAVE IT! RUN IN THIS HOLLOW TREE!

REPORTS HAVE BEEN COMING IN ALL NIGHT OF A STRANGE GNAT-LIKE CREATURE WREAKING...

HEY, LASAGNA, YOU DON'T SUPPOSE THIS COULD BE THAT OLD GUY I'VE NEVER EVEN HEARD OF?

DON'T GET ME STARTED, FRANK, YOU STUPID HATRACK! WHY, I...

LASAGNA, PLEASE, JUST BECAUSE IT QUIT BEING HOT AND NOW IT'S RAINING IS NO REASON TO GET VIOLENT!
HOT

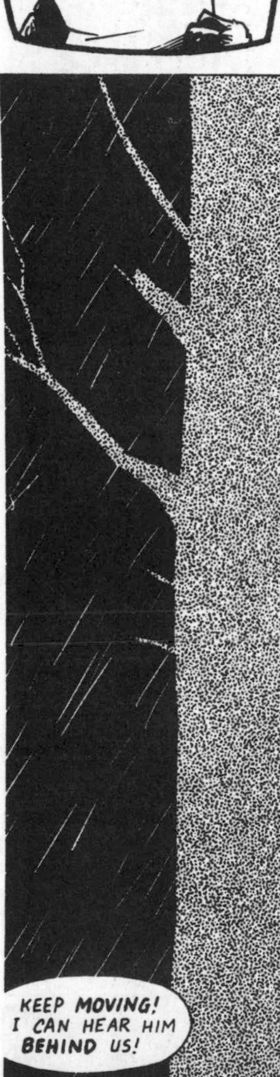
KEEP MOVING! I CAN HEAR HIM BEHIND US!
LET'S JUMP 'IM! THERE'S THREE OF US!
I'M NOT A DECREPIT OLD RAT TONIGHT! THIS RAIN IS LIKE.. LIKE...

NO WAY, MAN! THAT WAS GNATRAT!
GNATRAT?
LIKE WATER FALLING OUT OF THE SKY!!

KRAK
AND THIS LIGHTNING...

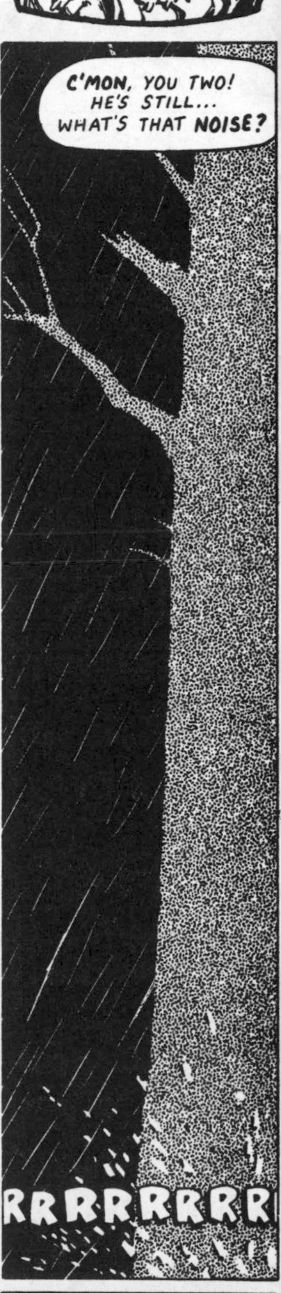
C'MON, YOU TWO! HE'S STILL... WHAT'S THAT NOISE?
RRRRRRRRR
I WANNA KILL!!

RRRRRRRRRRRRRRRRR

TIMBER.

CRASH

SO HOW'D HE RUN THE CHAIN-SAW WITH NO GAS? HUH SARGE? HOW?
DROP IT, KID!

GAS MY ASS!! WHAT I WANNA KNOW IS...

...IF GNATRAT WAS SAWING DOWN THAT TREE...

...WHO WAS FOLLOWING US??

KEEP WADDLIN', PUNK! YOU AN' ME GOTTA HAVE A TALK...

..JUST AS SOON AS WE FIND YOUR MOUTH!
CHU

GUESS WHOOOOO..
WHO.. ..?

YOU LIKE TO PLAY PEE-PIE, PUNK?
PEE-PIE??

YEAH, PUNK.. PEE-PIE! JUST LIKE YOU USED TO PLAY WIT' YO' MAMA!
HEY! YOU LEAVE MY MAMA OUTA THIS!

...CAN'T SEE, MAN... SOMETHIN' ON MY FACE..

MAYBE YOU NEED GLASSES, PUNK! MAYBE YOU NEED A PAIR OF GLASSES SHOVED UP YOUR--
WHADDYA WANT MAN?
WELL, I'LL TELL YA... IT WAS REALLY A LOT OF FUN BEATIN' THE CRAP OUT OF YOU AND YOUR PALS... BUT I'M LOOKING FOR A MORE SERIOUS RELATIONSHIP!
MAN...

I WANNA BEAT THE CRAP OUTA YOUR BOSS!
YOU'RE CRAZY!!

YEAH... I'M CRAZY.. CRAZY ENOUGH TO TAKE A PAIR OF GLASSES AND..
OKAY OKAY! I'LL TURN... PROVIDED..

..PROVIDED YOU STOP RUNNING YOUR MOUTH!

SPORT, YOUR ULTIMATUMS ARE USELESS HERE...
..OBSERVE.

PEE-PIE
Kiss the Cook

QUAAAAAAAAAAAAAAA
IT WASN'T EASY WORK PLUCKING AND STUFFING A TWO HUNDRED POUND DUCK -- THE BIGGEST DUCK IN THE FOREST.
THE QUACK ALONE IS WORTH IT.

GNATRAT?
DEATH ON TWO LEGS,
NEWSDUDE -- WHAT
A **HUNK**!!

NOT NOW, PLEEEZ!
I'M BUSY BEING
WISHY-WASHY ABOUT THE
POLICE COMMISSIONER
SITUATION...

IF YOU ASK **ME**, IT'S
ABOUT **TIME** SOMEBODY
DRESSED UP LIKE A
GIANT GNAT AND
KICKED SOME **BUTT**
AROUND HERE!

HE'S A **MENACE**!
I LIVE TWO BLOCKS
FROM HERE, AND EVERY
TIME GONZO CALLS
HIM UP WITH THAT--
-- BZZZXXP

GNATRAT!

THANKS FOR
ALLING, JIM.

HEY, GNATS,
THE CONSTITUENTS
ARE RAISING A BIG
STINK ABOUT THIS
ULTRA-DUPER
MEGAPHONE
YOU--

JIM, I WANT THE LOW-LIFE SCUM IN THIS FOREST TO **KNOW** WHEN I'M ON THEIR TAILS!
I KNOW THAT, BUT I WAS THINKING-- IF WE TOOK A BIG SEARCH LIGHT--

NO TIME FOR THAT NOW! I THINK I GOT A LEAD-- THE SCUMBAGS ARE PLANNING A LARGE WEAPON EXCHANGE TOMORROW NIGHT AT THE WEST END OF THE DUMP-- ELEVEN P.M. SHARP!

I KNOW IT'S NOT MUCH TO GO ON. BUT IT'S ALL WE HAVE!
BE **CAREFUL**, GNATS.

SOMETHING IN MY GUT TELLS ME I NEED A ROLAID!
WRITHE
SNARL
ALPO, IF I DIDN'T TRUST YOU IMPLICITLY, I'D SWEAR THERE WAS RAT POISON IN THAT CHEESE L'ORANGE!
MASTER BOO, CHEESE L'ORANGE IS A BIT.. ...CONTINENTAL FOR A RAT OF YOUR... WELL, IF YOU'D LET ME FIX YOU A NICE WARM OATMEAL...
ALPO, ALPO, ALPO -- DON'T YOU WORRY! WE SWAINS GROW STRONGER ON RICH CHEESE!
VERY GOOD, SIR! I JUST HOPE THE NEXT GENERATION OF SWAINS IS NOT HEIR TO AN EMPTY CHEESE CELLAR!
...ALTHOUGH, CONSIDERING YOUR SOCIAL CALENDAR OF LATE, THE PROSPECTS FOR A NEXT GENERATION ARE NOT VERY --
THAT'LL BE ENOUGH OF THAT! THERE MAY BE SNOW ON THE ROOF, BABY!!!
NOW BE A GOOD ENTLERAT'S GENTLERAT ND GET THIS GNAT-SUIT LEANED UP! I THINK I'LL WANDER AROUND THE MANSION NAKED AWHILE!
AND CHECK MY UTILITY BELT!
VERY GOOD.
AND PUT A GOOD SHINE ON THE--
OH NO!
SIR, YOU DON'T MEAN...
MASTER BOO?
IT AIN'T THE LONE RANGER, ALPO!
OF COURSE NOT, SIR-- IT'S JUST-- COULDN'T YOU RECONSIDER?!
NOT A CHANCE, ALPO! I'M TAKING HER OUT!
FAPP!
SUCKED.

THE GNATMOBILE -- THAT'S WHAT YOU CALLED IT, PRICK.

THEY SAY WE BE BABY! DIRTY DI-DEE DOO-DOO!

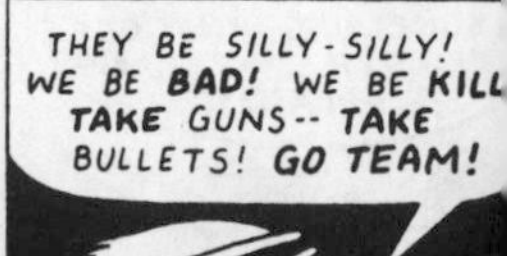
THEY BE SILLY-SILLY! WE BE BAD! WE BE KILL TAKE GUNS-- TAKE BULLETS! GO TEAM!

BRING GONZO HEAD!

THIS BE WAR!

KABOOM

AS NEVER ONE
MINCE WORDS...
I'D RATHER
MINCE PUNKS!
NYAA
NYAAA

WHAT TH--??
GNATOPHONE'S
PICKING UP
SOMETHING...
CHIC-KEN

MISSED ME, MISSED ME,
NOW YA GOTTA KISS ME!

THAT'S HIM, PRICK!
THE ART GANG LEADER!
I'D RECOGNIZE THAT
VOICE ANYWHERE!

AT LEAST I THINK IT'S
HIM -- SHOULDA PUT A
WINDOW IN THIS 'ROD!
..WHAT IF IT'S NOT
HIM? SHOULD I RISK
BLOWING AWAY SOME
MISGUIDED KID?
WHAT SHOULD I
DO, PRICK?

RIGHT! BLAST 'IM!
KLA

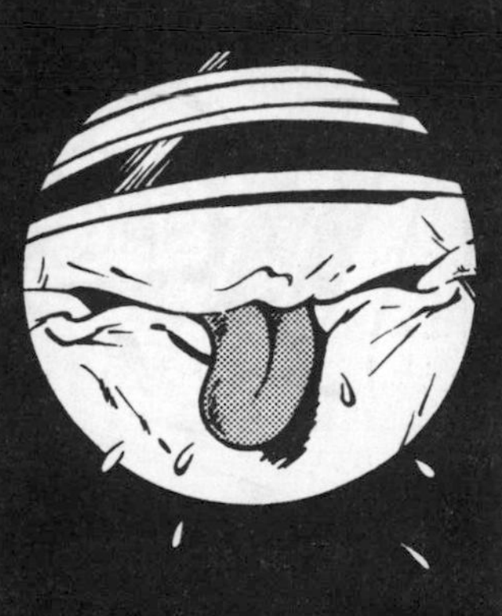

DAMN!
TRIGGER
JAM!
I'LL
KICK
ALPO'S
BUTT
FOR
THIS!

COME OUT AND FIGHT,
PANTIEBOY! I'M
RUNNING OUT OF
BABY TALK!
I DON'T KNOW...
IF HE'S HALF AS BIG
AS HE SOUNDS, I
MAY NOT --

WHATSA MATTER?
YOU LIKE
KIDDY COMICS??
THAT DID IT!!!

KISS
DRESSINGS
CHEEZ SQUEEZ
DIMENTS
TOOT ROLL
SPREADS
OLIVE LOAF
SPLUT
SHOW YOURSELF-- PUNK!
SNAP

AYOR THINKS IT'LL
GOOD P.R. TO
EGOTIATE WITH THE
RT GANGS.

OT THAT I OWE
M ANY FAVORS.
UT A POLICE
MMISSIONER
AN ARRANGE
HESE THINGS.

N'T BELIEVE
E'S GOING IN
ERE ALONE.
DN'T KNOW
E HAD IT
HIM.

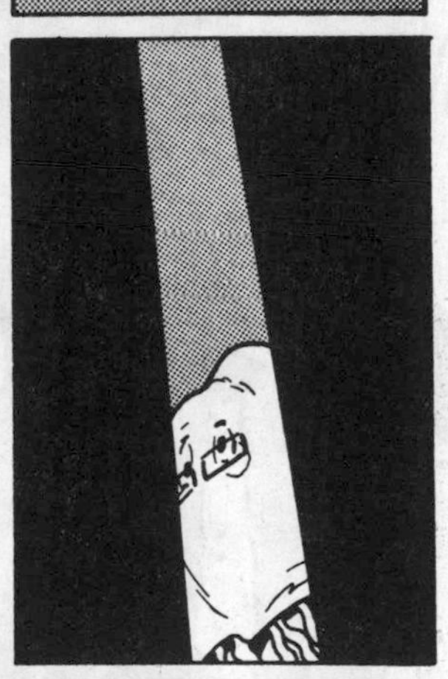

EAR A PASSIONATE,
MOST EROTIC GURGLE.
I HEAR
HANDCUFFS
SNAP.

KINDA THOUGHT
I'D HEAR THAT.

TEACH THE LITTLE
BASTARD TO GIVE MY
JOB TO A WOMAN!
DO NOT
DISTURB

I'LL TELL YOU A SECRET. I'LL TELL YOU HOW I CAN DO IT.
THAT'S WHAT EVERYBODY'S WONDERING.

THEY TELL ME I GOT ROOTS HERE... YEAH, I GOT ROOTS HERE -- THEY GOT SEVENTY YEARS OUTA ME...
ELLA
YELLO
COMMISSIONER
OF POLICE
AND I GOT THE ROOT!

SEVENTY YEARS OF THIS AND THEY WONDER.
OUT of ORDER

THEY WONDER HOW I CAN JUST LEAVE THE FOREST AND MOVE OUT TO THE POND...

I'LL TELL YOU MY SECRET. THE ONE I WON'T TELL AT THE BANQUET--
BECAUSE I WON'T BE AT THE STINKING BANQUET.

IT'S A SIMPLE SECRET.

POND
12 MI
I THINK OF BABY DUC
THE REST IS EA

IT'S GONNA BE A BUMPY RIDE BACK -- PUNKS ALL OVER THE ROAD... BUT THAT TUB OF CALGON/JELLO SUSPENSION SHOULD KEEP YOU STABLE.
THANKS... WHERE... DID YOU LEARN TO SET A BEAK... MAKE A SPLINT...
GIRL SCOUTS.
WHAT'S YOUR NAME?

ROBIN. ROBIN REDBREAST.

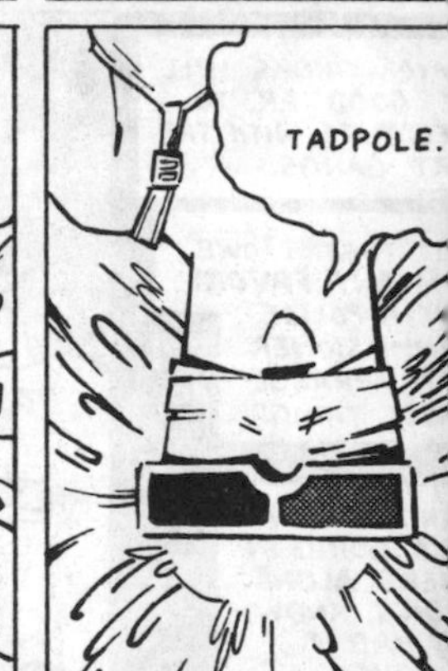
TADPOLE.

I SEE... WELL-- HOW ARE YOU FEELING NOW ...TADPOLE...
I'LL... BE FINE ...BUT... THAT... OLD DUDE...

HOW 'BOUT IT, ALPO -- YOU OKAY?
VERY GOOD, SIR. I DON'T MIND THESE BIG JOBS SO MUCH...

IT'S SQUEEZING INTO THAT **CHAINSAW** THAT GETS TO **ME**!

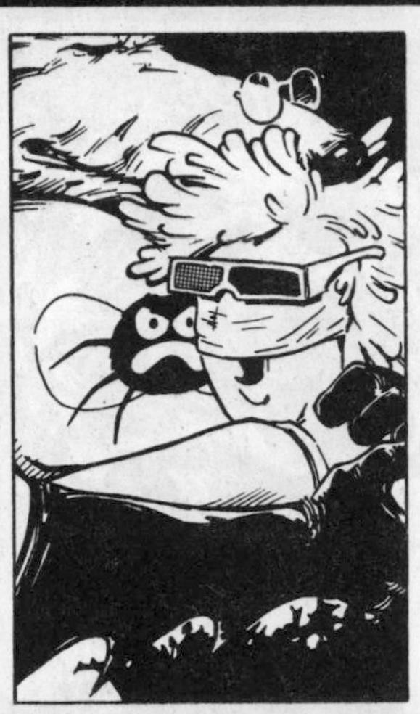

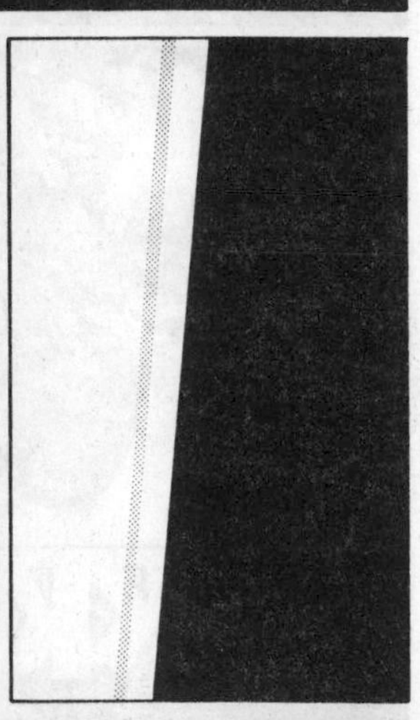

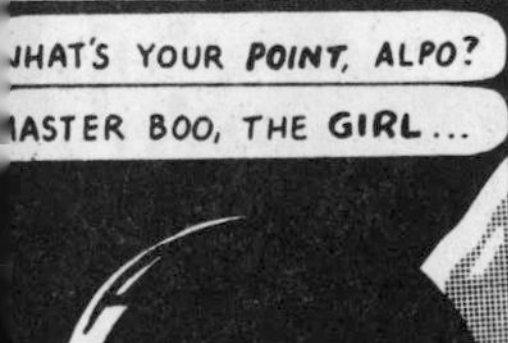
WHAT'S YOUR **POINT**, ALPO?
MASTER BOO, THE **GIRL**...

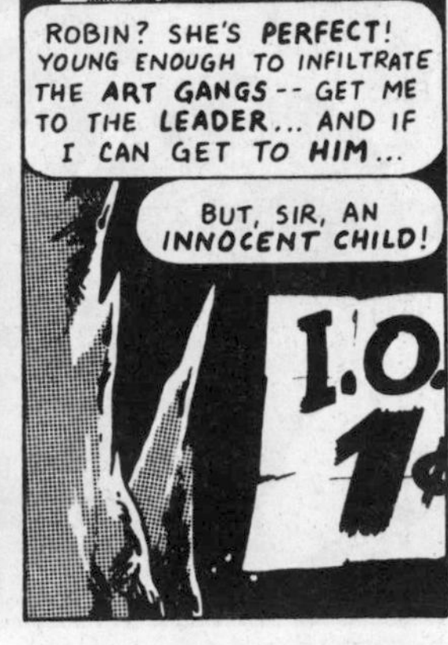
ROBIN? SHE'S **PERFECT**! YOUNG ENOUGH TO INFILTRATE THE **ART GANGS** -- GET ME TO THE **LEADER**... AND IF I CAN GET TO **HIM**...
BUT, SIR, AN **INNOCENT CHILD**!
I.O.U.
1¢

INNOCENT? WITH A NAME LIKE **ROBIN REDBREAST**? SHE'S PROBABLY A **STRIPPER**!
VERY WELL, SIR, I SHALL BE BLUNT...

HAVE YOU **FORGOTTEN** WHAT HAPPENED TO **PRICK**?

...YES...

I HAVE FORGOTTEN! WHAT DID HAPPEN TO PRICK?

UH... WELL, I DON'T - THAT'S NOT TH POINT! THE GIRL-

YOU SHOULD KNOW THIS, KID. I GET BURNED, FOLKS GET HURT! I GOT BIG FRIENDS! GOT IT?

I'M COUNTING ON IT!

ACTION'S IN THERE!

OPEN UP! THE KID SAYS--
TAP
TA

GYAK!

WOKK
HEY, MAN, TAKE IT SOMEWH--

WOKK

WOKK
WOKK
WOKK
WOKK
WOKK
WOKK
WOKK
WOKK
WOKK
WOKK
TAXI

ODDY PULP FOUND IN ABANDONED TAXI. .FILM AT ELEVEN...

HERE IT IS, TADPOLE! JUST LIKE THAT BLOODY PULP SAID IT WOULD BE.
BUT...

NO BUTS, TADPOLE! HE GOT AWAY ONCE, BUT HE WON'T ESCAPE ME THIS TIME!
BUT, GNATRAT...

WHAT IS IT, TADPOLE? YOU GOTTA PEE AGAIN? I ASKED YOU BEFORE YOU PUT THE SUIT ON!

IT'S NOT THAT! IT'S THIS PLACE! WE'RE AT THE EAST ING OF STATELY SWAIN MANOR!
HUH?

CURSES! TRICKED AGAIN! IT'S BEEN SO LONG SINCE I WAS OUT HERE!

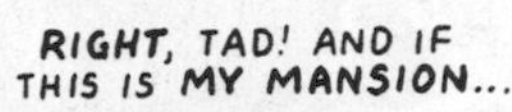

DON'T GO BILLY, BOO! THEY MAY HAVE WON THE BATTLE -- BUT THE WAR GOES ON!
RIGHT, TAD! AND IF THIS IS MY MANSION...

...THAT MUST BE MY PHONE!
NGRINGRI

GRINKLIK
NO, I DID NOT ORDER A CHEESE PIZZA WITH--

THE DUCK LIED.
WHA..?

WHAT DUCK?
CHUCK! CHUCK DUCK! HE LIED! THAT WASN'T THEIR LEADER YOU SQUASHED AT THE DUMP!

OH, RILLY, MR. SMARTY PANTS? WELL, IT JUST SO HAPPENS I DIDN'T SQUASH ANYBODY AT THE DUMP! WHEN I JUMPED OUT OF THE GNATMOBILE, HE WAS ALREADY GONE! SO THERE!
THE POINT IS, I KNOW WHERE THE LEADER IS...

WELLL...
NOT OVER THE PHONE.

HERE! MY PLACE!
AND JUST WHO THE HELL ARE YOU?

I'M ONE OF THE SLUGS THOSE HOODS USE TO BUY COKES!

HE TOLD ME WHERE TO FIND THE ART GANG LEADER...
HE WASN'T REALLY A BAD SLUG. HAD HIM A WIFE AND A COUPLE OF LI'L SLUGGERS... HE WAS THE ONLY SLUG EVER TO WORK HIS WAY INTO THE UPPER ECHELON OF THE SOFT DRINK INDUSTRY...
KRAM
HE STARTED TO TELL ME WHY A SLUG LIKE THAT WOULD RISK IT ALL TO BUY COKES FOR A BUNCH OF HOODLUMS.
I THOUGHT HE SAID "PASS THE SALT..."

ART G.
LEADER
HOW DEVIOUSLY OBVIOUS!

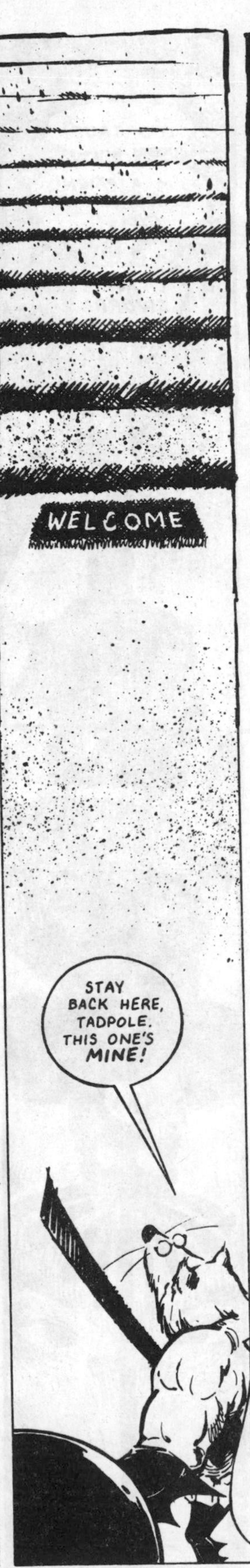
WELCOME
STAY BACK HERE, TADPOLE. THIS ONE'S MINE!

ART G!
ARE YOU SO UGLY, IN THE BRIGHT LIGHT OF DAY --
-- THAT YOU FEAR A SINGLE RAT?

GNATRAT
DARLING
FOR UNTOLD YEARS, I'VE WATCHED YOU WAGE YOUR LITTLE WAR!
THE FOOLISH FOREST CRITTURS THINK YOU THEIR BRAVE KNIGHT ERRANT!
BUT I -- I KNOW YOU'RE JUST A PETTY IDIOT! AVENGING THEM NOT! AVENGING ONLY YOUR COMIC BOOKS!

YOU THINK YOU'RE SO HIGH AND MIGHTY!
I KNOW YOU'RE BUT ANOTHER WOULD-BE HERO BASED ON A HERO!
YOUR VERY EXISTENCE IS MEANINGLESS WITHOUT HIM!
HEAR MY NAME --"AGATHA"-- GET IT?
LOOK AT ME, GNATRAT! OBSERVE MY DISTINCTIVE DRAWING STYLE.
LOOK AT YOURSELF!
IT'S TRUE!
I'M A PAWN! SLAVE TO THE CYCLE!
I HAVE A SWORD!
M

FOOL. YOU'RE ONE OF US. THE OBSCENITY YOU'RE SWORN TO ABOLISH!
I ENVELOP YOU. JOIN ME!
...I'LL MAKE YOU RICH...
YES.
I'VE HEARD YOU CAN MAKE A KILLING OFF THIS CRAP!

LIGHTEN UP, AGATHA! IT'S ONE OF THOSE TRICK SWORDS, SEE?
HOLY HEART FAILURE, GNATRAT! YOU SCARED HER TO DEATH!

WELL, MAYBE THAT'S WHAT I'LL DO! MAYBE I'LL GO AROUND SCARING FOLKS TO DEATH!
?

Y'KNOW, SHE ALMOST HAD ME THERE, TAD! IT IS TRUE WE'RE JUST SIDES OF THE SAME COIN!

BUT IT'S NOT TOO LATE, TAD! I CAN BE A REAL HERO -- AN ORIGINAL! SO WHAT IF I'M PUSHING A HUNDRED -- SO WHAT IF I'M GOING BLI--!!

THAT'S IT, TAD!

MY NAME IS BOO SWAIN.
THE DOCTOR SAYS I'LL BE BLIND WITHIN A YEAR. I'M WORKING ON MY OTHER SENSES.
I LIVE IN THE FOREST AND I LOVE A GOOD COMIC BOOK.
THAT'S ALL YOU NEED TO KNOW.
DR
NEW AGE COMICS COMPANY
MARTIN

SWEET AGATHA... YOU'LL BE MISSED...

YOU WERE AN EFFECTIVE PAPER TIGER.
AGATHA

BUT YOU DID NOT DIE IN VAIN. OUR WORK GOES ON WITHOUT YOU -- A HELL OF A LOT BETTER WITHOUT YOU...

...THAN WITHOUT THE BURGER KINGPIN! HA HA HA HA HA HA HA

AAAAAAAAAAH! GLORY DAYS!
YA DON'T KNOW WHAT YA GOT 'TIL YA LOSE IT!
DR
GONZO!
GONZO HAD THE RIGHT IDEA!... GIT WHILE THE GITTIN'S GOOD! RETIRE OUT TO THE POND AND SLACK OFF!!
URIN ALY SIS BEER "AN OKAY BEER"
CRIMINY!
WHAT WUZ I THINKING? I SHOULDA QUIT! I WUZ A GAZILLIONAIRE!!

I'm over a HUNDRED YEARS OLD!!!
HAPPY BIRTHDAY TOOO YOO
HAPPY BIRTHDAY TOOOO YOOOOOO
OH CHRIST DO WE HAF TA GO THRU THAT AGIN?
HAPPY BIRTHDAY DEA
GNATRAT
HAPPY BIRTHDAY
FWAP!
I'M NOT THE GI~

HAPPY BIRTHDAY Alpo

RIPT RUSSSL

ZZZZZZZ
BZZZZZZZZZ

SLAPT

A DARK AND GNATTY NIGHT, FIFTY YEARS AGO.
JOCK
KRAK!
G-
POW

GNATTI

Qaddafi

GR

KR K!

IN A COMIC BOOK THAT MAY OR MAY NOT MAKE SENSE A SUCKER IS ABOUT TO FORK OVER $1.75 —

GRRRRR
IF YOU CAN READ THIS YOU'RE TOO DARN CLOSE!
Qaddafi
SHRED
RRRRRR
AH, **THERE** YOU ARE, SIR...
HAPPY BIRTHDAY!
RRRRR
RRRRRRRR
YUK!
I.O.U. 1¢
I.O.U. 1¢

I TAKE IT YOU DON'T LIKE YOUR GIFT.
I.O.U.
1¢
SOME GIFT!

IT'S NOT LIKE I DIDN'T TRY! THE COMIC BOOKS JUST AREN'T BACK UP TO SNUFF YET!
I.O.U.
1¢

...I BROUGHT YOUR THUNDERBIRD...
HE CHILLS OUT.

WHANG

HE THINKS.
AND HE FORGETS WHERE HE WAS GOING.

...HE TURNS FROM THE STAIRS, AND STRIDES BACK TOWARD HIS TELEVISION.
WHAT MORE CAN ONE RAT DO, ALPO?

I SCARED THE ART GANG LEADER TO DEATH! I SHOWED THEM ALL THE WAY! WHERE ARE THE GOOD COMIC BOOKS?
SIR, THESE THINGS TAKE TIME.
XII
I
II
III
IV
V
VII
IX
X
XI
TIME?
I'M SEEING ON BORROWED TIME, ALPO! TIME IS A LUXURY EVEN MY GAZILLIONS WON'T BUY!!
SORRY, SIR. I AM AN INSENSITIVE BOOB!
WATCH IT, ALPO! DO NOT TAUNT ME WITH THE NAME OF THE GREAT ONE!
SIR, MY LOYALTY TO YOU IS BEYOND MEASURE-- AS IS THAT OF ROBIN. BUT TO BE QUITE HONEST--
YOU'VE BECOME SOMEWHAT OF A PAIN IN THE ASS!
I GOT YER PAIN IN THE ASS, YOU INSOLENT--
BOP

SORRY, OLD FELLA-- I GUESS I AM A BIT ON EDGE.
VERY WELL, SIR. JUST REMEMBER, I DO HAVE THAT OLD FAMILY RECIPE!
WELL!
YOU DON'T HAVE TO GET NASTY!
SIR, THIS CONSTANT BROODING-- WHY DON'T YOU WATCH SOME TELEVISION. MAYBE THERE'S AN OLD ZORRO MOVIE ON.
NO KIDDING, EINSTEIN! THAT'S WHAT I WAS GONNA DO!
THE ART GANG LEADER IS DEAD! HE'S WORM FODDER! HERE'S THE MAR OF THE FUTURE! THE FORES BELONGS TO THE GNATRAT

GIMME A BREAK!
I DON'T KNOW WHICH IS WORSE -- MUTATED MARTIAL ARTS GROUPS OR THESE DAD-BLAME GNAT MONSTROSITIES!
ALL I WANT IS TO READ ONE GOOD COMIC BOOK BEFORE I GO COMPLETELY BLIND!
BUZZZz
HUMMM
BUZZZz
BZZZZZ
KLIK
I HUNGER

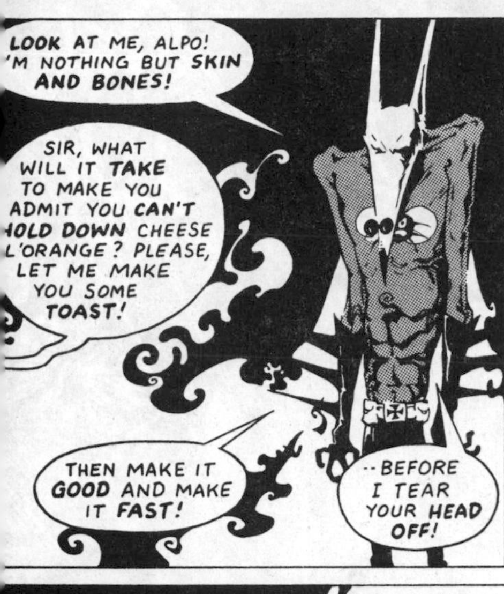
LOOK AT ME, ALPO! 'M NOTHING BUT SKIN AND BONES!
SIR, WHAT WILL IT TAKE TO MAKE YOU ADMIT YOU CAN'T HOLD DOWN CHEESE L'ORANGE? PLEASE, LET ME MAKE YOU SOME TOAST!
THEN MAKE IT GOOD AND MAKE IT FAST!
-- BEFORE I TEAR YOUR HEAD OFF!

IS THIS MY REWARD FOR BEING CHAMPION OF THE FOREST? A SMART MOUTH BUTLER AND SOME DRY TOAST?

...FAILING EYESIGHT AND GNAT-BASTARD COMIC BOOKS?

A FOURTEEN-YEAR-OLD WARD WHO KEEPS HERSELF LOCKED IN HER ROOM MORNING, NOON AND NIGHT?
DEATH.
HEAR HER IN THERE WITH ER SCISSORS AND HER RAYONS -- MAKING VALENTINES R PAPER DOLLS, OR WHATEVER HE HELL FOURTEEN-YEAR-LD CHICKS DO.
OT LIKE IT WAS WHEN RICK WAS AROUND! EFORE HE... HATEVER THE ELL HE DID!
ME 'N PRICK! WE FOUGHT 'EM ALL! JERKO! THE TUXEDOED BUMBERSHOOT REPRESENTATIVE! UGLY-ON-ONE-SIDE! THE -- THE -- SCAREDY -- WHATEVER THE HELL THEY WERE ALL CALLED!
HEY, YA BIG BABY!!

HAPPY BIRTHDAY
I MADE IT MYSELF!
I ♥
RETURN TO CINDY WARD
PULL

The ORIGIN of the
GNATRAT
BY BOOB KOON
—WHAT HE IS AND HOW HE GOT THAT WAY!
DARK, GNATTY NIGHT, LONG, LONG AGO, OM SWAIN, HIS WIFE AND HIS WITTLE BABY VAT WERE WAITING FOR A BUS...
YOU-- UH -- A GUN! HOLD ON - UH
QUIT YAMMERIN' AND HAND OVER DE ARTWORK!
BAD MANS!
BEAT IT, BRAT.
HA
HA
OOOOOO

PRECIOUS LITTLE EYES GROW BIG AND MOIST WITH TEARS AS THE **FULL TERROR** BECOMES PAINFULLY CLEAR...
DUNDABUD..
bird

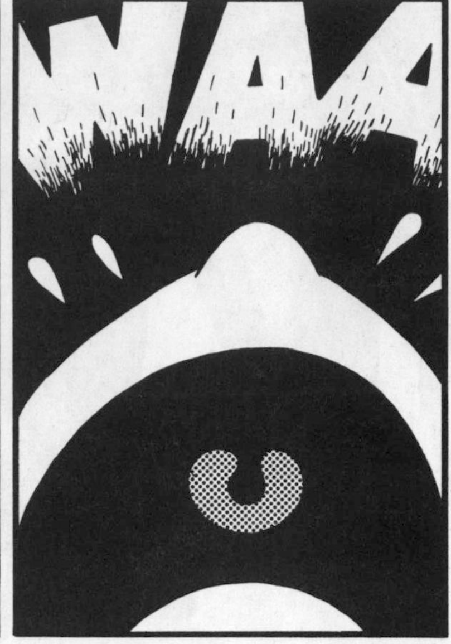
WAA

LATER, A BIZARRE PROMISE IS MADE-
I SWEAR, AS MICKEY AND MIGHTY ARE MY WITNESS, I'LL DEVOTE MY LIFE TO SQUASHING PUNKS AND MAKING THE WORLD SAFE FOR **GOOD COMIC BOOKS**-
AND I WON'T **FAINT** LIKE MY SISSY PARENTS!

YEARS GO BY AS BOO SWAIN STUDIES AND BECOMES A **MASTER COMICOLOGIST!**
DON'T READ ALL NIGHT, BOO. YOU'LL **RUIN** YOUR **EYES.**
SUPERMAN
WILLIKERS
OKAY MOM

HE TONES HIS MUSCLES TO UNBELIEVABLE PERFECTION, UNTIL HE IS LITERALLY A **RODENT DYNAMO.**
Krazy-pogo
K-P

THOUGH THE ART GANGS RUIN HIS COMICS CAREER, THOMA SWAIN AMASSES A **FORTUNE** STUFFING ENVELOPES... UNTIL ONE DAY--
DAD FINALLY CROAKED! NOW **I'M RICH!** RICH ENOUGH TO-- BUT WAIT I'LL NEED A **SECRET IDENTITY!**

ART GANGS ARE **ALL TALK** AND **NO NUTS!** SCARED TO DEATH OF THE SMALLEST OF THREATS! SO I GUESS JUST ABOUT *ANYTHING* WILL DO-- BUT **WHAT?** MAYBE... A...

HIS ANSWER -- GNATS FLY IN THE OPEN WINDOW.
GNATS! THAT'S **IT!** I SHALL BECOME A **GNAT!**

THUS IS BORN THE STRANG FAN OF THE FOREST. THIS SQUASHER OF PUNKS. THE **GNATRAT!**

AS USUAL, AN EVIL CRIMINAL IN A RIDICULOUS DISGUISE DEALS DEATH THROUGHOUT THE FOREST, LEAVING BEHIND A TRAIL OF BUG-EYED CORPSES -- THE DEATH-MASK OF THE **JERKO!** WHO DARES TO CONFRONT THE DEMENTED KILLER? **GNATRAT** AND **TADPOLE**, THE SWINGING SIDEKICK! IT'S A GAME OF WITS, PLAYED BY A HANDFUL OF DIM-WITS!

N THE FOREST, THE DINNER
OUR IS SPENT IN FRONT OF
HE TELEVISION SET --
, ISN'T IT EACEFUL TING BY E-VEE!
TOO PEACEFUL! WHEN ARE YOU GOING TO GET OFF YOUR REAR AND FIX A DECENT MEAL?

SUDDENLY, THE ENDLESS BARRAGE OF NEWS IS CUT SHORT BY AN EVIL VOICE -- A VICIOUS BUG-EYED FACE.
AT EXACTLY MIDNIGHT TONIGHT I, JERKO, WILL KILL DR. RUTH GOOGENHIMMLER AND STEAL THE BLACK CHROME AND OLEO! DO NOT TRY TO STOP ME! ESPECIALLY YOU, GNATRAT!

THE DREADED HOUR NEARS...
I'M GOINK TU DIEEEE! ZUMBOTTEE DU ZUMZINK!!

NOT FAR AWAY SITS A LIZARD -- A LIZARD WITH A CHANGELESS, GOOF FACE, ESPECIALLY THE BIG, UGLY EYES

NEWSPAPERS, RADIOS -- ALL CARRY THE BAFFLING MYTERY OF JERKO'S BAFFLING MYSTERIOUS DEED. BAFFLING TO ALL BUT BOO SWAIN, THE GNATRAT, WHO RELAXE AT STATELY SWAIN MANOR WITH HIS YOUN WARD, PRICK JASON, ALIAS TADPOLE, TH SWINGING SIDEKICK.

THE NEXT EVENING, A FAMILIAR SCENE UNFOLDS ON SCREENS THROUGHOUT THE FOREST

HE FANTASTIC NEWS THAT THE
JERKO IS GUNNING FOR POLICE
MMISSIONER GONZO REACHES HIS
OD FRIEND **BOO SWAIN** THROUGH
E "GRAPEVINE".

WHERE RE YOU OING **ALONE?**

I'M GOING TO PAY THIS JERKO A VISIT! I JUST GOT WORD OVER THE "GRAPEVINE" THAT MAKES ME THINK IT'S TIME HE GOT A **WOLLOPPING!**

IT IS NIGHT. JERKO SITS ALONE IN HIS "HIDEOUT"
GONZO, EH? WHEN I GET THROUGH WITH HIM, HE'LL BE GONE, ALL RIGHT!

SUDDENLY, A GROWLING, BARKING VOICE -- A VOICE OF AUTHORITY...
TALKING ABOUT ME?
GONZO!!

HALT!
FOOL! DO YOU THINK THAT IS THE ONLY WINDOW IN THIS PLACE? IF THEY CAN LET YOU IN, THEY CAN LET ME OUT!

UNKNOWN TO THE JERKO, GNATRAT AWAITS OUTSIDE.
COME BACK HERE, YOU! YOU MAY BE THE DEALER OF DEATH...

-BUT I'M THE ACE OF SPADES!

CLOWN! IT TAKES MORE THAN A SHOVEL TO STOP THE JERKO!

NOW I'VE GOT YOU! WHAT A NIGHT! FIRST, YOU! THEN, GONZO!

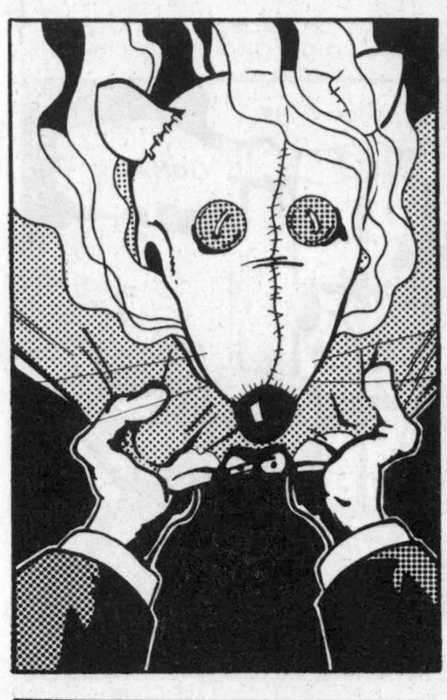

OH NO!
IT CAN'T--

BOO-M!

AN EXPLODING AUTOMATON! BRILLIANT!
YES, BUT I SHUDDER TO IMAGINE WHAT MIGHT HAPPEN IF THIS IDEA FELL INTO THE WRONG HANDS!

WELL, HERE'S ONE SET OF HANDS WE NEEDN'T WORRY ABOUT! INTO THE DRINK WITH HIM!

C'MON, YOU TWO! LET'S GO GET THAT JERK, JERKO!

HA HA HA HA HA HA HA HA
HA HA HA HA HA HO

????

HOLY HEART FAILURE
It's the
GNATRAT
HE'S THE FOREST'S FAVORIT
ADVENTURE-STRIP COSTUMED HERO -- AND THAT SPECTACULAR DISCOVERY, THAT GIGGLING YOUNG WONDER

Tadpole
"THE SWINGING SIDEKICK"
THEY WILL AMAZE YOU MONTHLY WITH THEIR CRIME-FIGHTING DERRING-DO IN
DEFECTIVE COSMOS

I OWE YOU ONE, ALPO! THAT HEESECAKE WAS SUPER!
I MUST CONFESS SIR...
I BOUGHT IT AT THE BELLY OF THE SNAIL!
WELL, I OWE THEM ONE -- AND THAT GIVES ME AN IDEA!
BELLY OF THE SNAIL--
I need borders.
GOD HELP US-- WHADDYA WANT?
WATCH YER LANGUAGE, SON. SUPPERMAN HERE --
SEND EVERYTHING ON THE MENU UP TO RON'S RANCH -- AND PUT IT ON MY TAB!
I FEEL YOUNG AGAIN! THE NIGHT IS MINE AGAIN! -- AND THAT COMIC BOOK--

SAY, ALPO...
WHERE'D ROBIN GO?
AND WHERE DID MY SLEEVE GO?
? ? ?

LIFE GOES ON, OLD FRIEND.
LATER...
SHE WAS A GOOD SOLDIER-- I'LL MISS ROBIN. AS I MISS... UH AS I MISSSss.

-PRICK, SIR.

PRICK!
YEAH, RIGHT. PRICK WAS A GOOD SOLDIER, TOO.
BUT ENOUGH OF THIS! WE MUST FORSAKE THIS FUTILE SEARCH FOR ROBIN AND CARRY ON!

AGREED! SHE HAS BEEN GONE FOR THREE HOURS!

AT FIRST, IT IS NOT EASY

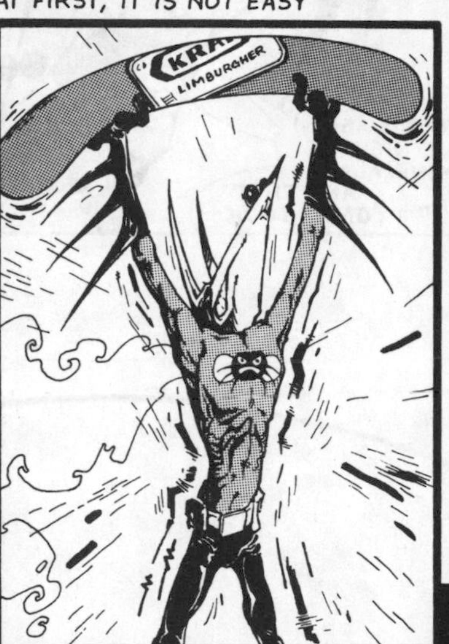

IN FACT, IT IS VERY DIFFICULT

AND PAINFUL!

BUT BOO SWAIN KNOWS HE MUST REBUILD HIS DIMINISHED BODY. HE MUST REGAIN THE STRENGTH AND STAMINA THAT ONCE WERE HIS. THROUGH SHEER **EXERTION** OF **WILL**, HIS MUSCLES DEVELOP AT AN **INCREDIBLE RATE**...

AN **INCREDIBLE RATE**... UNTIL...

I AM YOUNG AGAIN!
THE NIGHT IS MINE AGAIN!
NOT THAT SPEECH AGAIN!!
...BUT THE AMAZING GNATRAT HAS ONLY BEGUN...

FOR BOO SWAIN IS GOING BLIND!
ALPO!
KLIK!

AND NEITHER HE NOR HIS DOCTORS, ALL THE KING'S HORSES NOR ALL THE KING'S MEN CAN EVER MAKE HIM SEE AGAIN.

THE FOREST'S MOST ADVANCED PHYSIQUE CAN BE A MIXED BLESSING TO ONE WHO IS GOING BLIND...
ALPO

THE GREAT DETECTIVE DEDUCES THAT HE MUST DEVELOP HIS RE-MAINING SENSES TO COMPENSATE HIS FAILING EYESIGHT.
-- SENSE OF HEARING --
WOW!
I'M HOT F'R TEE-CHUR!
TUNE TIME

-- SENSE OF TASTE --
AAAAAH -- LAST JULY! A VERY GOOD MONTH!

-- SENSE OF SMELL --

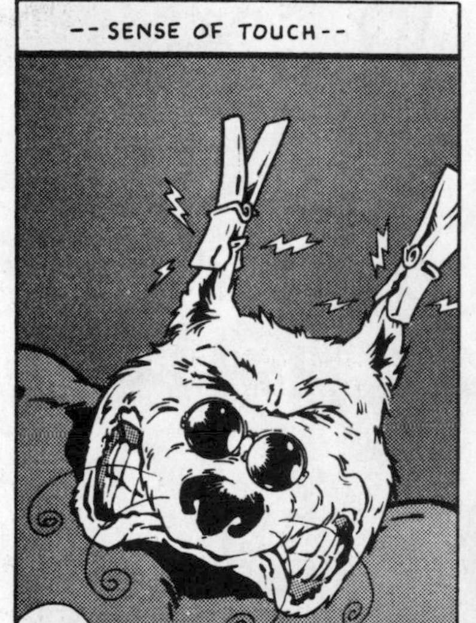
-- SENSE OF TOUCH --

-- AND ... WHAT ?? ... A SIXTH SENSE! A SENSE OF IMPENDING DANGER.
HEROES CLEARINGHOUSE
You may already be a WINNER
Master Boo Swain
Stately Swain M
The Forest
URGENT

PERCHED PRECARIOUSLY ON THE EDGE OF A NEW ERA -- A WHOLE NEW VOLUME IN THE SAGA OF THE GNA
HOLD IT!

I AM NOT THE GNATRAT.

GNATS ARE NOT BLIND! I AM TRANSFORMING INTO A DIFFERENT ENTITY! I SHALL NEED A NEW ALIAS -- BUT WHAT? MAYBE... A..

HIS ANSWER -- A BLIND DEVIL FLIES IN THE OPEN WINDOW.
OOPS! 'SCUSE ME.
WOK
THAT'S IT!

GUESS WHOOOO...

WHO...

YOU LIKE TO PLAY **PEE-PIE,** GNATRAT?

PEE PIE?

YEAH, **PEE-PIE!** JUST LIKE YOU USED TO PLAY WIT' YO **MAMA!**

YOU GOT IT ALL **WRONG,** PUNK! **ME** AND **MY** MAMA USED TO PLAY...

WHOK

PAT-A-CAKE!!

SIR! GROOOANNN

WHAT'S **LEFT** OF ME, SIR.

SIR, YOU WERE HAVING A **NIGHTMARE!**

ALPO? IS THAT YOU?

GEE WHIZ, ALPO. YOU SHOULDN'T TRY TO **TRICK** ME LIKE THAT!

WELL, OF **COURSE** I WAS HAVING A NIGHTMARE..

NOW KINDLY GET YOUR ***HANDS OFF MY FACE!!***

SIR, I DON'T HAVE MY HANDS *ON YOUR FACE*-- I NEVER *DID!* YOU WERE HAVING A ***NIGHTMARE!***

OKAY OKAY--

JUST TURN ON THE LIGHTS.

BUT SIR-- THE LIGHTS **ARE** ON!

MASTER BOO-- ARE YOU ALL RIGHT?

ALPO, WE GOT ANY THUNDERBIRD LEFT?

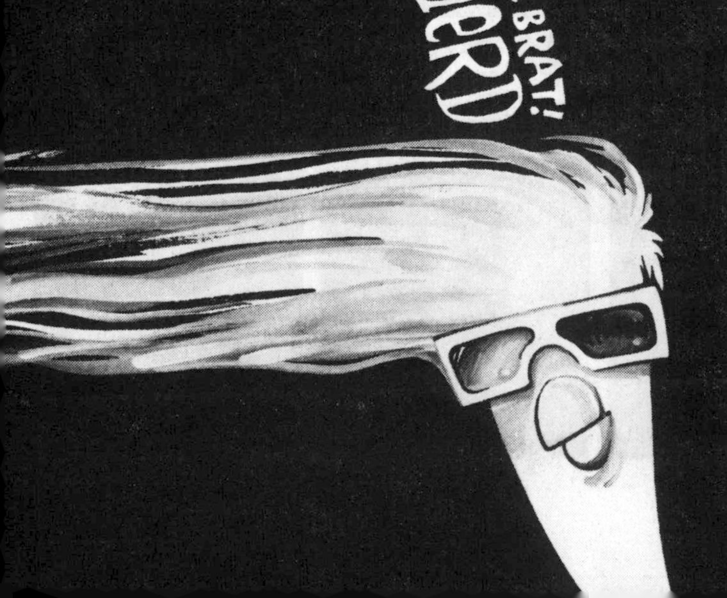
TADPOLE... SWEET LITTLE MONKEY WRENCH... LITTLE SOLDIER TORE UP SOME OF MY MOST VALUABLE COMIC BOOKS TO MAKE ME THAT BIRTHDAY PRESENT... LI'L BRAT!
WHERE DID SHE GO THAT DAY? WHAT DID BECOME OF MY BIRD NERD

HE GREASEMONGERS THE STINKING GREASEMONGERS AND THE LOUD CRACKLING GREASE MACHINES THE FRYING PITS
THEY SMELL LIKE ARM PITS AND FRY MY TATERS--
--I MUST CONCENTRATE-- I'VE GOT THE BLUES--
SNIF
SNIF
--I'VE GOT THE REDS--
IN A NEST NEAR WATER NEAR HAWAII, A POPPA HOLDS AN EGGBEATER-- WHICH IS NOT A RONCO --IT IS AN EKCO--
THE BEATERS WHIRRRR
...LIKE... WHEN YOU WHISTLE THROUGH A FAN
WHOA NELLY--
RRRRRRRRR
--POPPA AGAIN--LIKE ICICLES HIS TEETH--THE SALIVA DRIPS AND SHINES AND HE SLOBBERS AND DROOLS--
--NO--

NO, HE IS **NOT** POPPA

TOXIC
WOMBSVILLE

OTHING
ASTES
HERE--
ESPECIALLY THEIR BURGERS -- I MUST EAT THEM OR THEY JUST HOLD THEM IN FRONT OF MY NOSE.
STINKING
HEY, I DON'T GIVE A FLYIN'--
SOON I WILL CALL MY JONAH -- AGAIN HE WILL CALL ME STINKFISHPOT.

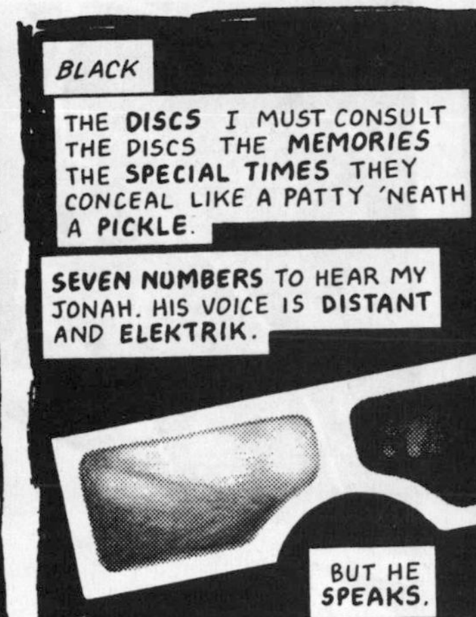
BLACK
THE DISCS I MUST CONSULT THE DISCS THE MEMORIES THE SPECIAL TIMES THEY CONCEAL LIKE A PATTY 'NEATH A PICKLE.
SEVEN NUMBERS TO HEAR MY JONAH. HIS VOICE IS DISTANT AND ELEKTRIK.
BUT HE SPEAKS.

ONE DISC SPEAKS TO ME.
I SPEAK TO THE OTHER.
THE DISCS ARE BLACK.

ZZZZZZZZZZZ

BBBZZZZZZZZZZZZZ
IT IS NOT MY JONAH.

HHMMMMMMMMMMMMMMT
DAMN GNAT.

French's
Bird Seed
-- I ONLY KNOW I WANT TO TASTE SOMETHING--

phone
I'M NOT IN A PHONEBOOTH.
I'M IN A HUGE CATHEDRAL.
I'M NOT CRUSHED IN STEEL AND GLASS.
SIX DAYS OLD.
GROVELING.
I AM WITH JONAH.
THERE IS NO FAT MAN OF A PIG.--
POUNDING ON THE DOOR--
LET'S GO
HURRY UP!!!
HURRY
--RUSHING ME--
HURRY UP-- I GOTTA USE THE--
IN A MINUTE!
I'M TALKING TO BRICK!
phone
Okay

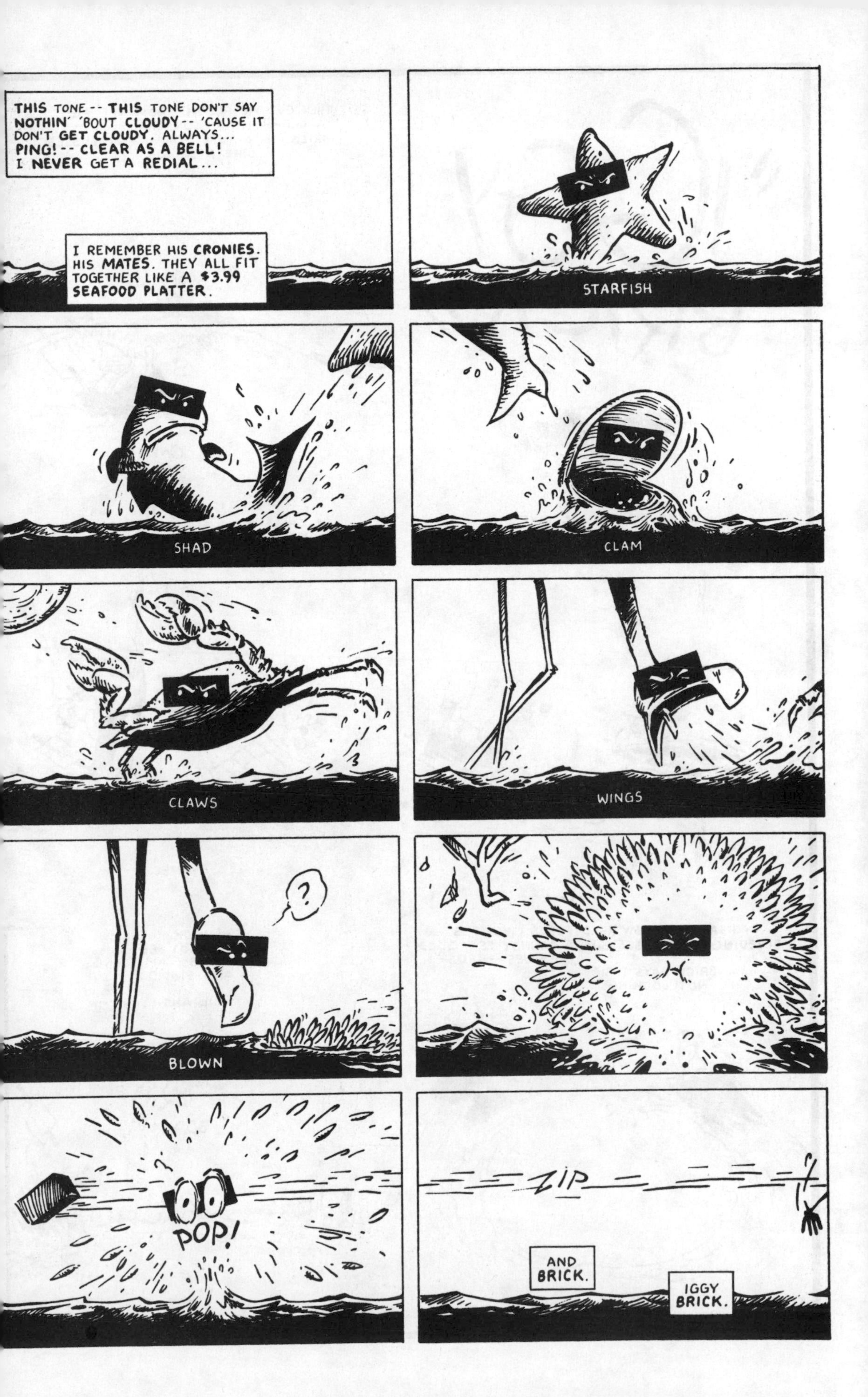
THIS TONE -- THIS TONE DON'T SAY NOTHIN' 'BOUT CLOUDY -- 'CAUSE IT DON'T GET CLOUDY. ALWAYS... PING! -- CLEAR AS A BELL! I NEVER GET A REDIAL...
I REMEMBER HIS CRONIES. HIS MATES. THEY ALL FIT TOGETHER LIKE A $3.99 SEAFOOD PLATTER.
STARFISH
SHAD
CLAM
CLAWS
WINGS
?
BLOWN
POP!
ZIP
AND BRICK.
IGGY BRICK.

"IGGY BRICK"

THEY GOT ME FRESH FROM THE EGG.
A CLEAR HEAD -- UNSCRAMBLED —
BRICK IS A TUFF JONAH AND CUSSES
LIKE A SAILOR

ONE.

THOUGH HE DIDN'T SAIL LIKE ONE.
I CHOOSE LOVE AS MY WEAPON
AND WANT HIM TO CALL ME THAT —

TWO —

HE CALLS ME
STINKFISHPOT

THREE

MY HEAD HURTS. MY HEAD FEELS LIKE IT IS
BLEEDING. I CAN SEE BUT I CANNOT SEE GOOD --
-- BLUES -- REDS -

BRICK SAYS I AM
NOT LOOKING.

FOUR

I LOOK.
I DO NOT SEE.
BRICK SAYS I AM YOUNG.
AND STUPID.

LIL ANJIL.

FIVE.

BOY, THEY SURE DON'T TALK MUCH--
A GRUNT HERE, HALF A WORD THERE...
MAYBE IF THEY WENT
OUT MORE OFTEN...
SOMETIMES I HEAR THEM TALKING WHEN THEY ARE NOT TALKING.
I AM GOING BILLY.
THEY LET ME DO ALL OF THEIR CHORES...
I COOK THE SOUP. I CLEAN THE WHALE.
IF I AM VERY GOOD, BRICK LETS ME WEAR THE SELF-LOCKING VICE GRIPS--
--LIL SWITT HOTT--
NOW HE SPEAKS TO THE OTHERS. SOMETHING ABOUT BONZO'S PIZZA-- NO, NOT PIZZA -- SOMETHING ABOUT BONZO'S RAY GUN.
BBL
I DO NOT UNDERSTAND. I WANT TO UNDERSTAND. TALK TO ME NOW, BRICK.
LISTEN TO THIS
LIL DOLLINK
BRIGHAM MARTIN

GOT TO BE THERE... TO BE WITH BRICK...

...ON THE WHALE...

THOUGH I AM A GOOD LITTLE ROBIN... THOUGH I KEEP THE WHALE SPOTLESS AND LEAVE NO FOOTPRINTS IN THE PIZZ--

WHAT?!!

WITH THE PIZZA AGAIN?

I WAS TALKING ABOUT BRICK

THOUGH I COOK THE SOUP AND NEVER COMPLAIN... BRICK DOES NOT BOP ME ...TODAY...

TODAY I AM A BIG BIRD.

BRICK IS BEACHING THIS PIZZA TODAY. IT IS TIME. I MUST GO... TO POPPA...

BRICK DOES NOT BOP ME TODAY.

BRICK GIVES ME THESE GLASSES.

I CAN SEE!

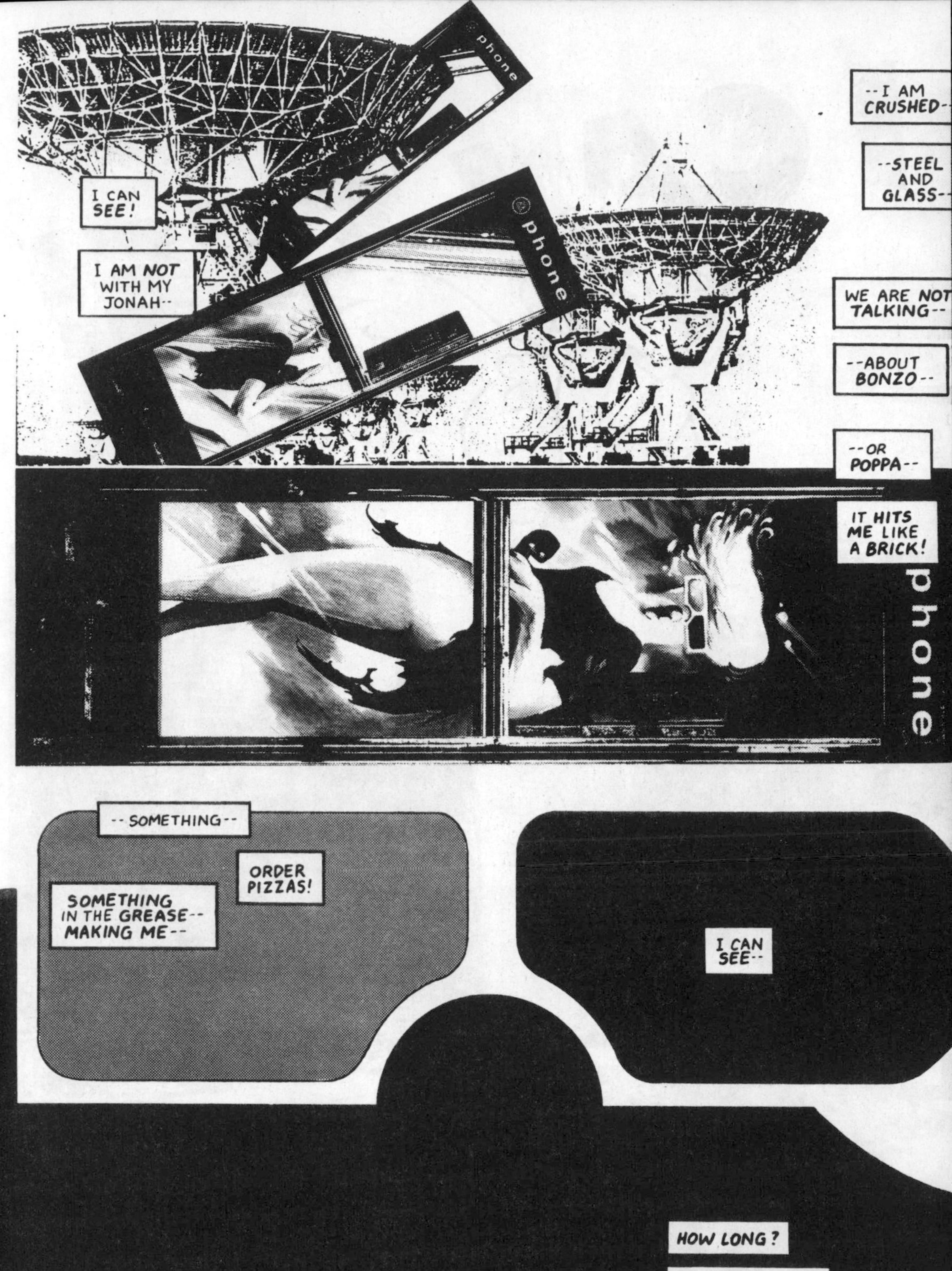
phone
I CAN SEE!
I AM NOT WITH MY JONAH--
phone
--I AM CRUSHED--
--STEEL AND GLASS--
WE ARE NOT TALKING--
--ABOUT BONZO--
--OR POPPA--
IT HITS ME LIKE A BRICK!
phone
--SOMETHING--
SOMETHING IN THE GREASE--MAKING ME--
ORDER PIZZAS!
I CAN SEE--

HOW LONG?
THEY MUST PAY!

YOU ARE A TADPOLE
IT THUMBS ITS NOSE.
YOUR POWER IS
TRAPPED WITHIN YOU.
TADPOLE TADPOLE
NYAA NYAA - NA
NYAA NYAAAAA
I AM RUBBER
YOU ARE GLUE--
I AM IN A
GREASY
SPOON--
--NOW--
THE YOUNG GREASER--
--SLIMY--LIKE A--
--SNAKE!
YOU SWIM BUT I
SWIM FASTER
IT HISSES--
YOU ARE TINY BLACK HERSHEY--
KISS

THE SNAKE IS FAST --
-- BUT YOU HAVE LEGS.

KISS--
POIT!
POIT!

--THIS.

--SLIMY LITTLE GREASER--

--BROUGHT ME HERE MADE ME EAT THEIR GREASY SLIMY--
MADE ME ORDER PIZZAS AND--

BROUGHT ME HERE--
CARDBOARD SANDWICHES AND GREASY TATERS--
WATERED-DOWN POP AND HYPNOTIC JINGLES--
WHO MILK
THE MILKME
MILK
...BAD MILK...

THEY THINK I AM YET UNDER THEIR SPELL--

THE GATOR IS A KETCHUP PACKET--
TEAR HERE

BURGER KINGPIN IS PAPER--
SCISSORS CUT PAPER--

YEOWCH
ROCK CRUSHES SCISSORS--

--ANKLE--
HURTS--
--BUNS--
LIKE
CONCRETE!

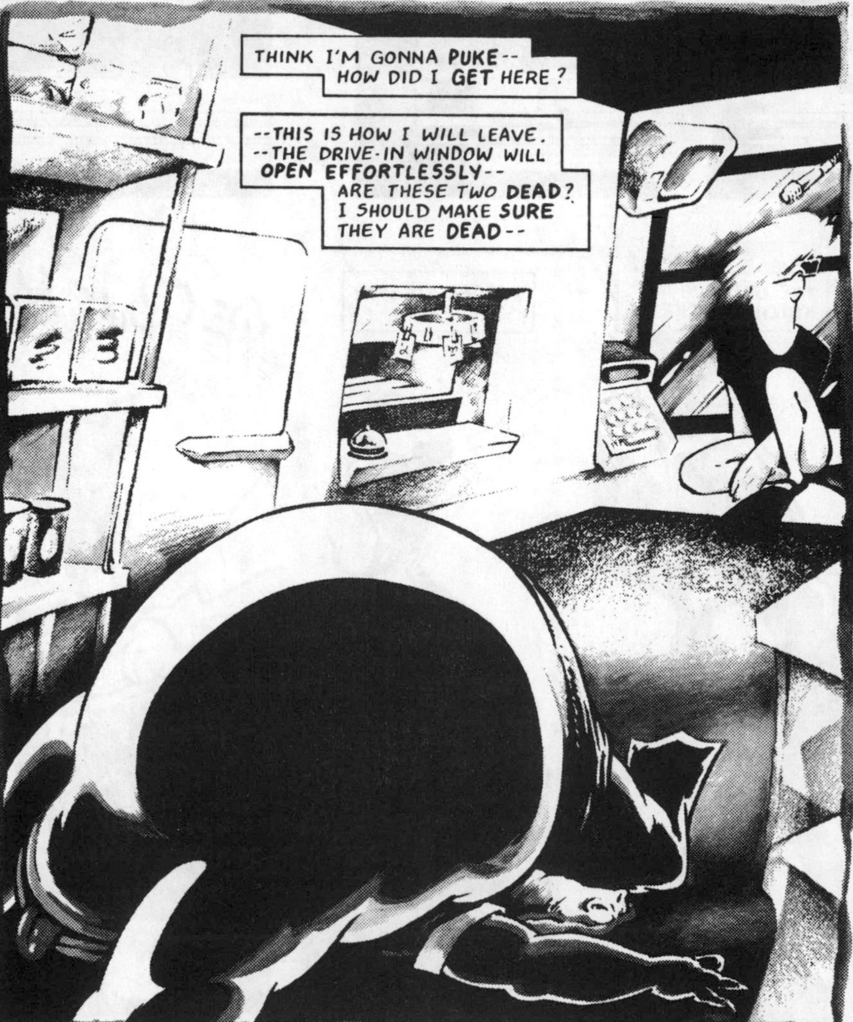
THINK I'M GONNA PUKE--
HOW DID I GET HERE?
--THIS IS HOW I WILL LEAVE.
--THE DRIVE-IN WINDOW WILL
OPEN EFFORTLESSLY--
ARE THESE TWO DEAD?
I SHOULD MAKE SURE
THEY ARE DEAD--

--BUT BOO
NEEDS ME--

VE
IT
MY
WAY
PULL

SO THAT'S IT!
POOR KID...
TSK TSK
BURGE
KINGPIN
GRR!
OH! OOO!! THAT KINGPIN MAKES ME SO MAD..!! PICKIN' ON MY LI'L BOOBALA LIKE THAT..! MAKIN' HER DO THEM MEAN THINGS!

IT'S FROM THE POND, SIR... ...UH...
THERE IS NOT A FROG ON THE LIMB WHO DOES NOT TREMBLE WHEN HOPPY CROAKS. WELL, THERE IS ONE-- BUT HE IS MORE THAN 'FROG'

--OR LESS, DEPENDING ON YOUR OPINION OF FROGS-- CALL HIM THE BURGER KINGPIN. DRUGS, WHORES, ARMS, PRESIDENTS... ALL ARE AT HIS DISPOSAL. WHATEVER IT TAKES TO STRENGTHEN HIS BURGER EMPIRE. HIS TO USE... HIS TO CONTROL.
ALL BUT THE COMIC BOOKS. THEY WERE TAKEN FROM HIM. PULLED LIKE A RUG BY--

GNATRAT, SIR. WHO HE IS, WHERE HE LIVES, WHAT KIND OF DEODORANT HE USES... EVERYTHING!
MY COUSIN DOWN AT THE POND... ...TONIONIO... HE... WELL, HE WAS JUST LOOKING THROUGH THE YELLOW PAGES, AND THERE IT WAS-- UNDER 'COSTUMED HEROES'...

...GNATRAT, THAT IS...
I HEARD YOU THE FIRST TIME. GIMME IT.
NO ONE HAS TO BE TOLD. THEY ALL LEAP FROM THE LIMB TO THEIR DEATHS.

RERAT / TADPOLE™ One-Shot Graphic Novella, February, 1987. Published by MIGHTY PUMPKIN, Mark Martin, Writing/Drawing Pictures. Jeannie Martin, Taking Care of ness. OFFICE OF PUBLICATION: 1203 16TH AVENUE SOUTH, BIRMINGHAM, AL 35205. **SECOND CLASS STORY AND ART.** Published one-shot. Price $1.95 per copy in the U.S. and $2.75 in Canada. Subscriptions not available. Canada and foreign not available er.

RRRRRRRRRRRRR

DARERAT... THE NAME STUMBLES ACROSS THE ONE HUNDRED YEAR OLD LUMP THAT IS HIS MIND. ALLITERATE IT ISN'T. BUT IT'S THE BEST NAME HE COULD COME UP WITH.
HE RUBS HIS EYES AND LOOKS OUT THE

WINDOW.

I CAN'T SEE!
I CAN'T SEE!
I CAN'T SEE!
KICK!
KICK!
KICK!
KICK

I'LL GET OVER IT.
STILL A BIT OF A SHOCK TO WAKE UP BLIND -- DON'T BELIEVE ME, JUST TRY IT.
THANK NIMH I'VE GOT ALPO TO STRAP ME TO THE WALL OR I MIGHT TEAR SWAIN MANOR APART WITH MY BARE HANDS.
WHY DID I GET UP, ANYWAY ?
DON'T HAVE A JOB. NEVER HAD A JOB THANKS TO DEAR OL' DAD AND HIS DEAR OL' MONEY.
CAN'T FIGHT CRIME TILL I'VE HAD MY BREAKFAST.
BLACK CHROME

WHERE THE **HECK** IS **ALPO**? WONDER IF HE'S GOT MY **BREAKFAST** FINISHED.
WONDER IF THE **MAIL'S** HERE YET.
WHAT **TIME** IS IT?
HOW'S A GUY SUPPOSED TO **KNOW** THESE THINGS WHEN IT'S **ALWAYS MIDNIGHT**?
RESERVE OR SUPPERMAN

MAIL'S IN -- **FAT LOTTA GOOD** IT'S GONNA DO ME WITHOUT **ALPO** AROUND. CAN'T **READ** THE STUPID STUFF. I MEAN, **GIMME A BREAK**! I **AM BLIND**, YA KNOW...
NUTS! DON'T SMELL ANY **PERFUME** ON ANY OF IT.

PROBABLY JUST A BUNCHA JUNK MAIL ANYWAY -- SOME **BEGGARS** WHINING FOR MORE OF **MY**--
Boo Swain
Stately Swain Manor
The Forest
HAT'S THIS? A **TAPE**?
AN'T BE ANY GOOD.
--**NO PERFUME**--

BOO, THIS IS ZEPPI...

DOWN AT THE **PIZZA NUT**. LISTEN, BOO, LOUIE... HE'S GETTIN' PRETTY **STEAMED UP** ABOUT THIS **BILL** YOU GOT GOIN'...
BELLY OF THE SNAIL? **BOO SWAIN** HERE...

THAT'S WHY I MADE THIS **TAPE**, BOO-- WANTED TO MAKE **SURE** YA GET MY **MESSAGE** HERE--
HOW ABOUT SENDING OVER A **BIG PIZZA**... SOMETHING **BREAKFASTY**!

GEEZ, BOO A SIX MILLION DOLLAR PIZZA BILL? I'VE BEEN WORKING MY CAN OFF HERE!
WHADDYA MEAN, PAY MY BILL FIRST? I DON'T HAVE ANY--

I KNOW THIS IS A BAD TIME FOR YOU, BOO, WHAT WITH GOING BLIND AN' ALL. I HATE TO HAVE TO SAY THIS, BUT--
WELL, LOUIE -- HE'S OUT OF PATIENCE, BOO! EVERY FIVE MINUTES, ANOTHER DOZEN PIZZAS!

WHO'S EATING ALL THOSE PIZZAS, BOO. YOU GOT SOME PERPETUAL PARTY GOING ON, I'D APPRECIATE AN INVITE!
BING BONG

WHAT I'M TRYING TO SAY IS -- PAY YOUR BILL, BOO, OR LOUIE SAYS NO MORE PIZZA!
PIZZA!
ALPO MUSTA ORDERED IT. GOOD OL' ALPO!
SMELL THAT CHEESE!
THESE HEIGHTENED SENSES ARE A TRIP! SMELLS LIKE THERE MUST BE

SEVENTY-TWO THOUSAND CHEESE PIZZAS WITH EXTRA-EXTRA CHEESE!
SIGN HERE PLEASE.
SPLINTER'S PIZZA
SPLINTER'S PIZZA
SPLINTER'S

Oh POO!
These stupid BIG MAMAS.
On the T.V. commercials they shoot them with bazookas and they don't run... but just try to pull them up over your BUTT--

--already late for work. Gotta get this stupid preview in to that stupid BUYER'S GUIDE... didn't even put me in the stupid comic book.
Gotta go to the dentist at lunch. GOD I HATE DENTISTS!

My name is LASAGNA LAGNA. I'm a reporter.
CHECK IT OUT, LASAGNA!
HEY, LIKE I'VE GOT NOTHING BETTER TO DO!
TODAY I AM ANGRY
GONZO
Frank lays a stupid AP on me--
--that says BOO SWAIN is faceing bankruptcy court. Owes millions to every pizza joint in the forest.
this doesn't sound like BOO.

BOO-- IT'S ME, LASAGNA
"I ain't talking to no damn reporters!" Now THAT sounds like BOO.

BOO, THIS IS JUST BETWEEN US GIRLS-- YOU CAN TELL ME...
"I'm TELLING you! BUG OFF!"

BOO, HONEY, DON'T SAY--
A rueful horse laugh and he is away.

The laugh seems to LINGER IN THE AIR, like somebody just took off their shoes. This is not the rat I secretly love.
I WONDER-- Where is he hiding all those delicious PIZZAS?

THE BANK SAYS I HAVE TO PAY FOR ALL THOSE PIZZAS-- LIENS ON EVERY PENNY I EVER HAD.
I GET MAD AND THROW AN ASHTRAY. THEY TELL ME I MISSED BY A MILE.
ALL MY ACCOUNTS --FROZEN-- LIKE MY TOES.
STATELY SWAIN MANOR NEXT 7 MI
I PULL OUT SOME COMIC BOOKS. THEY'RE NOT HARD TO FIND-- EVERY DRAWER IN THE MANSION IS CRAM FULL. I'LL NEVER READ ONE AGAIN. NOT THAT IT MATTERS. THEY ALL SUCK NOW ANYWAY.
PROBABLY SUCK WORSE THAN I KNOW. ALPO READS THEM TO ME NOW. I CAN TELL HE'S MAKING STUFF UP--TRYING TO MAKE STUFF UP THE WAY I'D LIKE TO HEAR IT...
CAN'T SEE. BUT I CAN STILL TURN THE PAGES--SMELL THE NEWSPRINT.
I LOVE THAT SMELL.
JIM
HOLY COW

CAN'T SIT AROUND HERE SMELLING COMICS ALL DAY-- OR NIGHT, OR WHATEVER IT IS.
WISH I COULD SMELL SOME MONEY--
...I LOVE MONEY...

DAY, NIGHT, IT DOESN'T MATTER-- IT'S TIME-- I FEEL IT, LIKE A SLAP IN THE FACE
SNOW COVERS UP A LOT OUT THERE. BUT I KNOW-- THERE'S STILL A LOT OF VERMIN CRAWLING AROUND OUT THERE.

I CAN HARDLY WAIT TO GO SQUASH SOME.
IN MY NEW SUIT. ALPO SAYS IT'S READY NOW. A BRIGHT RED DEVIL COSTUME. JUST LIKE I TOLD HIM.
TOYS

--WITH A BOLD 'DR' EMBLAZONED ACROSS MY BREAST.
HOW ABOUT A LITTLE FANFARE--

R THE RAT
ITHOUT FEAR!
ICY NEEDLES.
A CACOPHONY OF WIND AND LIMBS REFUSING TO BREAK.
THIS IS MY LOVER TONIGHT--
--OR TODAY--
IRREGULAR
HE PRETENDS TO WARD
FF MY ADVANCES,
NOWING IT FILLS ME
ITH DESIRE.
TEASES ME WITH HER WINDY VEILS.
SPRAYS ME WITH CHAMPAGNE.

SHIT!
COLD!
FORGET IT!

VISA
YOUR DOOR'S STANDING WIDE OPEN, MISS BUNNY. DON'T YOU KNOW IT'S SNOW--

MISS BUNNY!

...I...
...I...

TOOK IT ALL, ALPO! EVER'THIN'! ALL GONE!
SAINTS PR'SARVE US! WHO COULD DO SUCH A THING?

DREADFUL HATEFUL PUNKS!
SHER AS I'M BUTT NAKED, EVER'THIN' I HAD I GOT FROM BOO! WEREN'T WORTH STEALIN', YE KNOW THAT!
HERE NOW-- THEY'RE GONE AND YOU'RE SAFE. THAT'S THE MAIN THING. I'LL FIX COFFEE.

NOT HERE, ALPO-- NO COFFEE--NO POT-- NO BED...
I CANNUT STAY HERE!

MORE ESPRESSO?
SHER AN' I'LL DRENCH ME DRAWERS IF I DID--
ALPO... YE'VE BEEN SUCH A DOLL ABOUT ALL THIS, I... WELL, FAITH 'N B'GORRA, ALPO, HOW CAN I EVER REPAY YE?

THE FIRST THING ALPO FEELS WHEN HE WAKES UP IS A THROBBING BUMP ON HIS HEAD.
HOW DID HE KNOW IT WAS A RHETORICAL QUESTION?
THE SECOND THING HE FEELS IS A WAVE OF NAUSEA...
NO TRESPASING
secret intrence to GNATCAVE

--EGGS--
--ONIONS--
--BELL PEPPERS--
ALPO THINKS HE'S DIED AND GONE TO HELL.

NOW HE KNOWS--THERE'S A DEMON.
AT LEAST SHE'S NOT MAD ANYMORE --MAKING BREAKFAST--
I HATE OMELETS.

RING

SERVANT'S QUARTERS.
--OH HI, BOO-- NO, YE DIDN'T CALL ME... ALPO'S COMING.

MASTER BOO, I-- WHAT?... I CAN'T HEAR YOU, SIR--YOU'RE TALKING THROUGH THE EARPIECE AGAIN. TURN THE PHONE AROUND.

PIZZA?? DID YOU SAY PIZZA? ARE YOU SURE?
OH DEAR OH DEAR

FIRST YOU SCOOP UP SOME OF THIS CARDBOARDY GREY STUFF--
...OOH... ABOUT THIS MUCH

IT'S SILLY--

YOU SLAP IT UNDER YOUR ARM LIKE THIS.

WHY DOES THE GIRL HAVE TO MAKE ANY OF THE PHONE CALLS... MUCH LESS ALL OF THEM. IT'S RISKY!

AND THEN--

WE COULD SPLIT THEM UP AMONG OURSELVES AND QUADRUPLE RESULT

OKAY, YOU YO-YOS GOT THAT?
YEAH, YEAH, EVERYBODY KNOWS HOW TO MAKE A BURGER PATTY! LET'S TALK ABOUT THE GIRL! NOW I THINK...
THEY ARE THE ELITE--HIS RIGHT-HAND FROGS. EVERY TIME THEY HARI-KARI THEY MUST BE REPLACED AND TRAINED. BUT THIS ONE IS A SLOW LEARNER.

YOU DO NOT THINK, WART! YOU DO NOT HAVE MY SENSE OF POETRY!

MY APPRECIATION OF IRONY...

THE GIRL STAYS!
SKWNS.!

HOW APPROPRIATE THAT HIS LITTLE MONKEY WRENCH SHOULD CAUSE HIM SO MUCH STRIFE
TOOT!
B
BOO SWAIN'S LIFE BECOMES A SERIES OF FUTILE STRUGGLES. ATTEMPTS TO REMOVE THE THORN FROM HIS PAW.
CLIMAXING IN A HILARIOUS PARODY OF A CONFRONTATION AT A LOCAL SHO-BIZ.

WHAT A JERK!
APPARENTLY COULDN'T EVEN FIND HIS GNAT COSTUME!
BOO SWAIN!
WHO ORDERED PIZZA FOR BOO SWAIN?
IRREGULAR
HAPPY BI

THE JUDGE SPREADS IT ON THICK. JUST AS I HAD PLANNED-- --ONLY BETTER.
EVERY CENT THE COURT CAN SCRAPE TOGETHER WITH BOO SWAIN'S NAME ON IT IS DISTRIBUTED AMONG HIS CREDITORS.
BUT IT IS NOT ENOUGH. HE AND ALPO MUST STUFF ENVELOPES UNTIL THE DEBT IS PAID.

MASTER BOO... I'M SORRY...
NO, I'M SORRY, ALPO. SORRY I DRAGGED YOU INTO THIS.
I DON'T DESERVE A FRIEND LIKE YOU, ALPO.

SIR, I'M OVER HERE. YOU'RE HUGGING THE PLANT.
WHA? ... UH... I KNOW THAT-- I DON'T DESERVE A PLANT LIKE THIS EITHER, OKAY WISEGUY?

PIZZAS... GOT THIRTY DAYS TO PAY THEM OFF AND SIXTY-FIVE CENTS IN MY POCKET...
AND A BOWL OF PENNIES IN THE KITCHEN AND I'M BLIND...
AND I'M NOT THE GNATRAT ANYMORE...
I'M NOT BROKE EITHER. NOT YET.
MAYBE... MAYBE I'VE GOT ANOTHER BOWL OF PENNIES SOMEWHERE. SEEMS LIKE I HAD A SOCKFUL OF DIMES BEHIND THE MIRROR IN TADPO--
WHERE'S ROBIN, ANYWAY?
NEED TO HELP ALPO WITH THOSE ENVELOPES.
RIGHT AFTER I TAKE A NAP.

'COURSE, ALPO PROBABLY WOULDN'T REALLY MIND IF I JUST LET HIM STUFF ALL THOSE--

-- WHAT AM I THINKING?

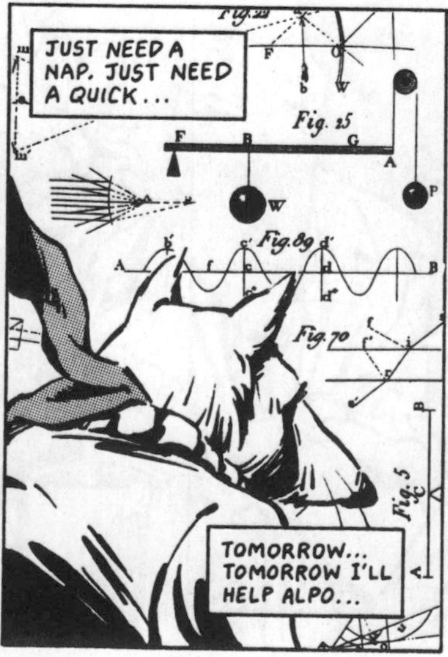
JUST NEED A NAP. JUST NEED A QUICK...
Fig. 25
Fig. 89
Fig. 70
Fig. 5
TOMORROW... TOMORROW I'LL HELP ALPO...

LEGS-- TREMBLE...
THAT RUMBLING-- STUPID BUSSES.
BUSSES?? WE HAVEN'T HAD ANY GAS FOR--

I HEAR A RADIO...
...NO, NOT A RADIO. VOICES, BEHIND ME.
"WOW! DID YOU SEE THAT?"
"...JUST LEVELED SWAIN MANOR..."
"...BIG FAT DUDE..."
"...WITH HIS BARE HANDS..."
"BIG! FAT!"

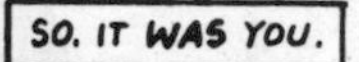

SO. IT WAS YOU.

...THOUGHT CROSSED MY MIND... BUT I NEVER BELIEVED YOU'D REALLY--
Thunde

YOU ALWAYS WERE JEALOUS OF THE MANOR, WEREN'T YOU?
HELL, I WAS GONNA GET KICKED OUT...

...BUT YOU JUST COULDN'T RESIST, YOU BIG STUPID--
I'LL GET YOU FOR THIS, SUPPERMAN!
HONK
IF IT TAKES ME A HUNDRED YEARS!

NEXT: Another Comic Book!

as

begins

he's at it again.
He's griping and fussing.
He's fussing and cussing.

He's shouting and groaning. He's pouting and moaning. He's rending his garment. He's stomping his feet. He's weeping and wailing and gnashing his teeth. He's got his panties in a wad. He's gonna whup some ass, by God! He's mad as a hornet — no, wait, a wet hen! He cusses and fusses and cusses again. He's one mad rat. He's one foul mood. He's one supremely PO'd dude. He fumes and growls and burps and snorts. He's never been more out of sorts. He's got a wild hair up his shorts. He's the Forest's spoildest sport. He's shouting and groaning.

COMIC BOOKS THIS- COMIC BOOKS THAT! YOU AND YOUR CRUSADES!!! WHERE DID IT GET US?

ALLOW ME TO SPELL IT OUT FOR YOU-- WE LIVE IN A CARDBOARD BOX -- WE ARE DESTITUTE, SAVE FOR THE CARDBOARD BOX, THE CLOTHES ON OUR BACKS, AND A BUNCH OF GRAPES!!

-WE'RE STUFFING ENVELOPES
O PAY OFF A SIXTY GAZILLION
DOLLAR PIZZA BILL--AND--
AND--THIS--

THIS--THIS CROSSHATCHING!
HOW AM I TO KEEP THE MANOR
TIDY IF WE CAN'T EVEN
AFFORD ZIPATONE??

. . . meanwhile at the Pond

Gonzo's not fond of this tabloid page.

In fact, he's **ENRAGED!**

-- **STILL** UNCLEAR **WHY** THE **GNATRAT** RETURNED AFTER **FIFTY YEARS**-- ONLY TO **DISAPPEAR** AS **MYSTERIOUSLY** AND **SUDDENLY** AS HE **RETURNED!!**

WE **STILL** HAVE **NO WORD** ON THE **LOUD GROWLY BARKY NOISES** HEARD AROUND THE POND LESS THAN AN **HOUR AGO**-- **INVESTIGATION** AT THE **SOURCE** OF THE NOISE LED BY **POLICE COMMISSIONER YELLO** HAS **NOT** TURNED UP ANY EVIDENCE OF **FOUL PLAY**

LOUD GROWLY BARKY NOISES

NOTHING HERE BUT A SHREDDED NEWSPAPER AND A CHEWED-UP CIGAR BU--
HEH HEH
CAREFUL, COMMISSIONER! YOU WANNA GET THE MEESES ON OUR BU-- OUR CASE? *

SAY MA-MA!

COO KIE!

EAR-WITNESSES DESCRIBE THE NOISE AS SOUNDING LIKE "AN **ANGRY OLD SCOTTIE DOG...**"

FORMER POLICE COMMISSIONER GONZO, WHO NOW RESIDES AT THE POND, COULD NOT BE REACHED FOR COMMENT.

PHILE FOTO

COO KIE!
H-YAH HA HA HA
GIRL ♥ SCOUT COOKIES

* Old Joke Alert

. . .written when Edwin Meese was on his anti-porn crusade.

...APPRECIATE IT IF YOU'D STOP POUTING AND HELP ME STUFF THESE ENVE--
BILT-GOOD SHOWER STA
Stately Swain manor

--MASTER BOO, I --I APOLOGIZE! I DON'T KNOW WHAT CAME OVER ME--THE PRESSURE-- I'M TOO OLD FOR--
HOW'S THAT, ALPO?

--YOU TALKING T'ME ?

SORRY, OLD FELLOW--I GUESS I JUST WASN'T LISTENING-- COULD YOU START OVER?

SEE HERE, ALPO--YOU NEEDN'T BE TIMID.
ALPO?

HMMPPH! TESTY LITTLE FAGGOT! I SHOULDA FIRED HIM YEARS AGO!

HMMPPH! UNREASONABLE OLD DESPOT! I SHOULDA WALKED OUT YEARS AGO!
GIRL SCOUTS

NOK NOK

WHAT'S THIS? COOKIES?
COO KIE

LOOK, KID, IF YOU'RE TRYING TO SELL SOMETHING, YOU PICKED THE WRONG CARDBOARD BOX -- I DON'T --
BUT..

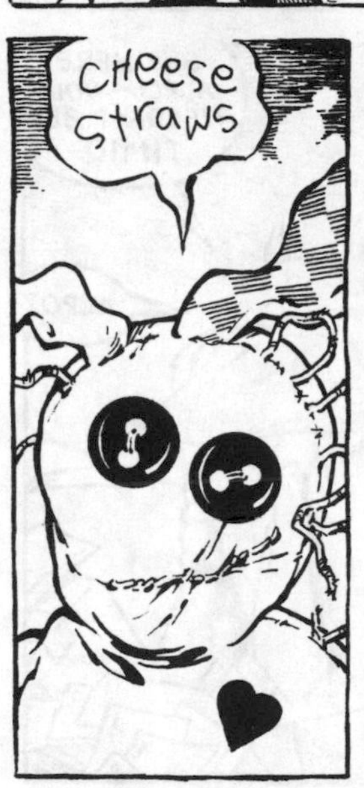
CHEESE STRAWS

SNIFF SNF...
LEMME SEE THAT!
GIRL♥SCOUT COOKIES

PUT THIS ON MY TAB, KID.

GNASH
KKNCH

NOT BAD, KID. TELL YOUR DEN MOTHER I SAID... SAID... DEN ...MO--
URP

GULP!

BONG!

KID! I CAN SEE!! I MEAN I CAN REALLY SEE!
SHAKE
RATTLE

SEE!?

HF-- PF-- GOTTA-- HUF-- GOTTA TELL BOO!! PF-- PF--

TELL BOO HF.. ABOUT..PF BURGER KINGPIN AND.. AND..
STATELY SWAIN MANOR NEXT 7 MI

HOLY HAVOC!

ATELY
VAIN
NOR
T 7 MI

BURGER KINGPIN!

GONZO!

PRICK

SAAAAAAY... WHO YOU CALLIN' "PRICK"?

YOU. PRICK. YOU'RE PRICK JASON!

SEZ YOU!

HE JIG'S UP, PRICK! I'M ON TO YOU! FIGURED IT ALL OUT WHEN I SAW HAT MOOD STATUE PROMOTION... I NEVER OLD ANYONE BUT YOU ABOUT MY MOOD TATUE IDEA -- I TRUSTED YOU!
BURGER KINGPIN
The MOOD STATUES ARE HERE!
BELCHEE
OH, IT'S ALL SO CLEAR, SO OBVIOUS NOW! IT ALL GOES BACK TO THAT NIGHT WE DEFEATED JERKO...
C'MON, YOU TWO! LET'S GO GET THAT JERK, JERKO!
HA HA HA HA HA HA HA HA
HA HA HA HA HA HO
????
YOU WERE YOUNG -- SENSITIVE!! WE DIDN'T REALIZE OUR LAUGHTER WOULD CUT SO DEEP!
YOU OLD POOTS THINK YOU'RE SO TOUGH!!
NOW SEE HERE, PRICK--
BOO HOO!
BLUH!

WE ONLY SAW YOU A COUPLE OF TIMES AFTER THAT. BOTH TIMES YOU WERE STUFFING YOUR FACE AT WHAT WAS *THEN* CALLED ***HUMONGO HEAVEN...***

LOOK, BOO! THERE HE IS AGAIN!

PRICK-- IT'S ME, *BOO!* CAN WE TALK?

IT'S NO USE, JIM! WE-- WE'VE **LOST HIM!!!**
PATHETIC!

A FEW YEARS LATER, HUMONGO HEAVEN CHANGED ITS NAME TO ***BURGER KINGPIN,*** AFTER THE MYSTERIOUS STRANGER WHO HAD ACQUIRED CONTROLLING STOCK OF THE COMPANY. IT WAS ALSO AT THAT TIME THE **ART GANGS** AGAIN BECAME STRONG FINANCIALLY-- STRONG ENOUGH TO DISRUPT THE COMIC BOOK INDUSTRY, THUS DRAWING THE *GNATRAT* OUT OF RETIREMENT AND **TERRORIZING HIM!!**

OOGA BOOGA !!

IT'S TRUE! DEAR GOD, IT'S TRUE! *I **AM*** PRICK JASON!
OUI OUI! FRENCH FRIES!

I KIDNAPPED ROBIN REDBREAST! ***I*** MADE HER ORDER PIZZAS!! ***I*** WANTED THE GNATRAT DESTROYED. ***DESTROYED BY HIS PRECIOUS LITTLE MONKEY WRENCH!!***

THIS IS FAN-@☼#* -TASTIC!!

APPARENTLY THE JERKO (WHO IS APPARENTLY NOT DEAD) LACED THOSE CHEESE STRAWS WITH SOME OF HIS GOOGLY-EYE POISON, FAILING TO TAKE INTO ACCOUNT THE STRENGHTH & PHYSICAL SUPERIORITY OF THE FOREST'S GREATEST DETECTIVE! WHY, IT'S LIKE A SECOND CHANCE! A CHANCE TO MAKE SOMETHING OF MY MISERABLE OLD SELF! A CHANCE TO DO MORE -- TO BE MORE THAN A HOMICIDAL COMIC BOOK JUNKIE MOOCHING OFF MY DAD'S GAZILLIONS!

A CHANCE TO KILL SUPPERMAN!

...SO WHAT DO I DO NOW?? I GUESS I GOTTA TURN MYSELF IN...
TURN YOURSELF IN??

HELL NO, PRICK, DON'T TURN YOURSELF IN! WOULDN'T THAT MAKE THAT WOMAN COMMISSIONER LOOK LIKE A HERO! OH, THAT WOULD BE JUST PEACHY!!
STOP THE PRESS!
ELLA YELLO HAS BURGER KINGPIN BEHIND BARS!
BEHIND BARS

DON'T TURN YOURSELF IN, PRICK... JUST PAY ME HUGE SUMS OF MONEY FOR THAT MOOD STATUE IDEA YOU STOLE FROM ME!

AAAAH!! HERE IT IS!!

NATURALLY I DON'T NEED A TELEPHONE DIRECTORY BECAUSE I'M PERFECT! WHY BOTHER LOOKING UP NUMBERS WHEN YOUR MEMORY IS INFALLIBLE!!

OOOOOOOOH!!
MY ACHING TOOFIES!!
I HATE DENTISTS

OH NO!! NOT THE PHONE PWEEEZ!!
WING WING
HIPPO LOVE
COSMO

HEWWO-- HEWWO, BOO? IZZAT YOU, BOO?
SUPPERMAN?? BOO, IT'S ME, WASAGNA!

CUT THE CRAP, SUPPERMAN! YOU'RE ABOUT FIFTY YEARS LATE FOR A DATE WITH MY FIST!!

A DATE? AWE YOU ASKING ME OUT FOWAH A DATE?

JUST NAME THE PLACE, YOU BIG FAT FART FACTORY! I'LL BE THERE WITH BELLS ON!

OH, BOO, I'D WUV A BANANA SPWIT AN A JUMBO FWY AT BUHGUH KINGPIN!!

A DATE WIV MY BE-WUVVED! OOOO... AND HE'S IN A GWOUCHY MOOD!! IT'S SO INVIGOWATING! TEE-HEE!
I'D BEST GET WEADY-- BUT HOW TO DWESS?? BOO SAID HE'D HAVE BELLS ON!
SILLY BOY!

IF THAT WAS LASAGNA LAGNA, I'M TORTURED BY DRY HARD STOOLS! SUPPERMAN MUST THINK I'M STUPID!
HIM AND HI FAKE VOICE!
BIG JERK!

OH WHAT A LITHERING OLD FOOL AM! I'VE WASTED MY IFE AWAY KOWTOWING O THAT PARODY OF A OMIC STRIP DO-GOODY!

N'T WORRY
BE HAPPY!
BUT, BY JOVE, TODAY IS THE FIRST DAY OF THE REST OF MY LIFE! I'M NOT TOO OLD TO START AT THE BOTTOM! THIS COULD BE FUN!

I WONDER IF THAT HAMBURGER ESTABLISHMENT COULD USE AN EXPERIENCED HAND?

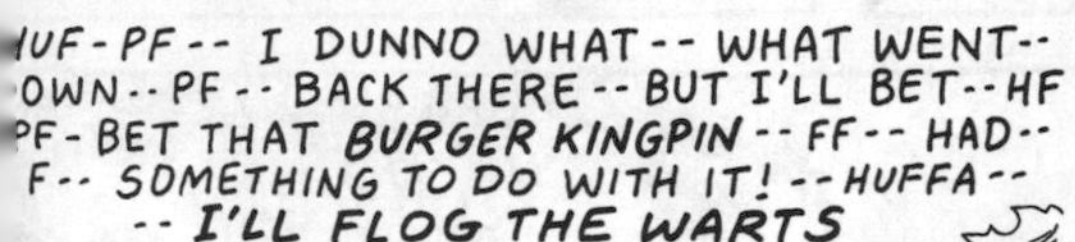
IUF-PF-- I DUNNO WHAT-- WHAT WENT-- OWN--PF-- BACK THERE-- BUT I'LL BET--HF PF-BET THAT BURGER KINGPIN-- FF-- HAD-- F-- SOMETHING TO DO WITH IT! --HUFFA-- -- I'LL FLOG THE WARTS OFFA THAT TOAD!

-AND I'M JUST MAD ENOUGH TO DO IT!!
HUFFA PUFFA
HF PF
PF
ALL BY MYSELF!
HF
WON'T BOO BE PROUD!
H
FFF

A DATE! A DATE AT WAST! I'M THE HIPPIEST HAPPO IN THE WHOLE FOREST!!

I DID IT! I KILLED GNATRAT! I KILLED HIM WITH HIS VERY OWN AUTOMATON INVENTION!
I CAN'T WAIT TO TELL THE BURGER KINGPIN!

RICH!! I'LL BE RICH!
AND I'M TURNING OVER A NEW LEAF! I'LL MAKE PEACE WITH GNATRAT AND MEND MY WICKED WAYS!
--ALL THE BABY DUCKS I DESIRE...
KLUD!
SUGAR SHAKE
SUGAR SHAKE

KILL!

KINGPIN
THIS IS GREAT! I'M GONNA SERVE THE MAN OF MEALS DESSERT!
THIS IS GREAT! THIS IS WHAT SEPARATES THE SIDEKICKS FROM THE STARS!
THIS IS GREAT! KINGPIN'S GONNA PINCH A BRICK!
THIS IS GREAT! YOU SAVED ME FROM MY WRETCHED LIFE OF CRIME!
THIS IS GREAT! BABY DUCKS!!
HAVE IT MY WAY!
THIS IS GREAT! I'M SURE I COULD MAKE MANAGER IN NO TIME!
THIS IS GWEAT! I HOPE BOO WIKES THIS DWESS!
TO THE DUMP

Now Boo knows
he's about to die.
His life flies
past his googly eyes.

But he's the comic reader's friend
Can this *really* be **THE END**?
And what *could* kill the Bag o' Wind?

'twas lazy writing that done 'im in!

WELL THERE YA GO... I'M DEAD!! DEADER'N A DOORNAIL!!
ALWAYS THOUGHT I'D DIE ON A FIELD OF HONOR OR--
OR SOMETHING!!
SOMETHING WITH A BIT OF DIGNITY!!
THIS IS JUST PLAIN STUPID!
HEY KID! GIT OFFA THAT THANG!
5
NOW WHAT?
WILL I GO TO HEAVEN--
OR THAT OTHER PLACE?

BUT I TRIED TO DO THE "RIGHT THING"!

I'VE TRIED TO BE GOOD. I KNOW I WAS A SELFISH OLD GROUCH!

WHAT'S THAT UP AHEAD? LOOKS LIKE A-- IS-- THAT A--

A COMIC BOOK STORE!

I'M GONNA SPEND ETERNITY IN A COMIC BOOK STORE!! I WAS A GOOD BOY!!

WELCOME!
MORE X-MEN IN BACK!!
MR. RETAILER: HERE'S YOUR SHIPMENT OF X-MEN COMICS
X MEN TRADING CARDS
HERE'S SOME MORE X-MEN COMICS
HOW TO DRAW X-MEN
X-MEN NEWZLETTER
X-MEN! ROLE PLAYING GAME
X-MEN PICKLES
X MEN CARDS
NEW X-MEN IN STOCK:
X-MEN FAN CLUB MEETS HERE
!
N-N-- -NoOO!!
COSMIC COMICS
HEY, THAT'S A HELL OF A NO! AND THIS'S A HELL OF A WAY TO END A COMIC BOOK! WELL, HELL, WATCH FOR MORE GNAT-RAT ADVENTURES WHEN HELL FREEZES OVER! HEH HEH!! HA HA HA! CACKLE YUK

GALLERY

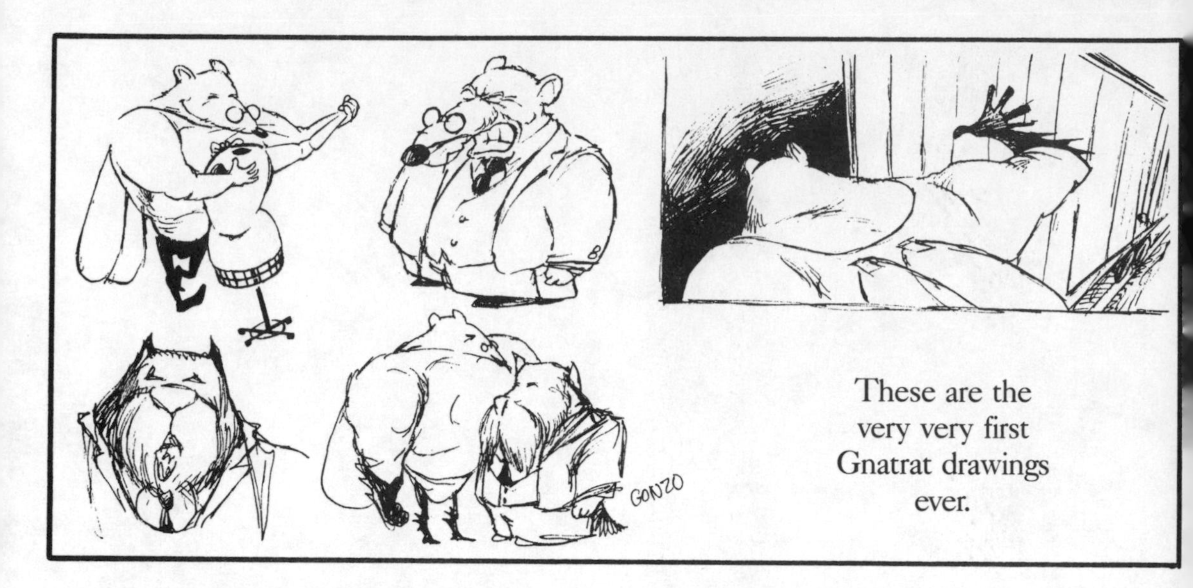

These are the very very first Gnatrat drawings ever.

Gnat Fink

Buddy's friend, Buddy and Weenie

Eyeballis © Alex LaVerde and Greg Boettcher

Balderdash ©Chuck Bunker, Chuckles Productions

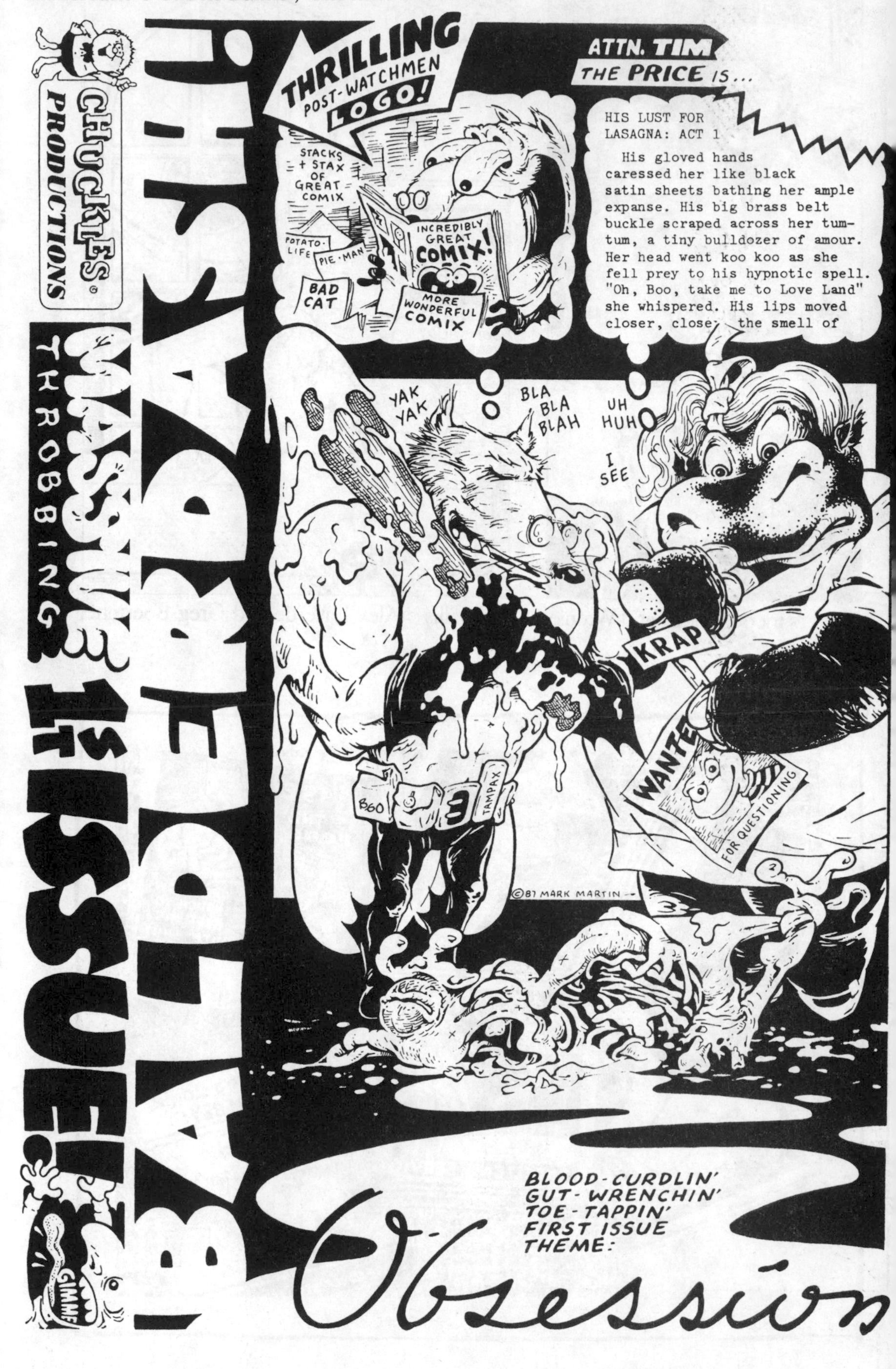

Slam Bang © Allen Freeman, Fan-Atic Press

SLAM BANG
FAN-ATIC PRESS
No. 9
On Our Cover :
GNATRAT : 1979
A RARE GLIMPSE INTO THE RETIREMENT YEARS OF THE WINGED WONDER ... MOODY AND MELANCHOLY, HE WOULD RETIRE TO HIS CUBBYHOLE OF SOLITUDE, DON HIS GNAT COSTUME AND READ MUSHY LUV STORIES FOR HOURS ON END. NOT EVEN GOOD OL' ALPO WAS ALLOWED IN BOO'S 'LITTLE BIT OF HEAVEN' RESULTING IN A SEVERE CASE OF FLEA-FESTATION. OF COURSE, THE FOREST'S GREATEST DETECTIVE WAS NEVER AT A LOSS FOR SOMETHING MORE IMPORTANT THAN FLEAS TO OCCUPY HIS CONCERN AND THE FLEAS NEVER PRESENTED A REAL THREAT TO HIS MIGHTY HIDE. (NOTICE THE FLEA ON THE LAMPSHADE WHO TRIED.)
Thunde
FeeE-LINGS WO WO WO·O·O·O FEEEE-HEEE-LEH-HINGS
sigh
LOVE STORY
LOVE STORY
ZERO STAKE
JO IGLESIAS
Joni Mitchell
TRUE Confession
COURT
Oh! Henry
ZERO
SNICKERS
FEELINGS
MORRIS ALBERT
MARK MARTIN ©87
PLUS STILL MORE COMIC GLUT!
INSIDE

I was SO MAD!

I PUBLISHED BLACK + WHITE in JANUARY 87
AND LIVED TO TELL THE TALE!
AHOY THERE!
I'M ADRIFT IN A SEA OF TURMOIL
NOW I KNOW HOW HOWARD THE DUCK FEELS
DARERAT ORDERS
DARERAT EXPENSES
WHERE DID EVERYBODY GO?
COME BACK!
... HOW DID I GET HERE?
I WAS BORN OF PRELUDE GRAPHICS IN THE SUMMER OF 1986
YOU'RE PRETTY GOOD WIT' YER MITTS, KID-- HOWJA LIKE TA DRAW COMIC BOOKS?
GNATRAT: THE DARK GNAT RETURNS WAS RELEASED TO AN ADMIRING PUBLIC...
TIME
NOT BAD
NOT BAD AT ALL
MY NEXT OUTING, HAPPY BIRTHDAY GNATRAT, WAS AN ENIGMA...
I THOUGHT THIS WAS GONNA BE "GNATRAT: THE EARLY YEARS"
DIMENSION GRAPHICS? WHAT ABOUT PRELUDE?
WHY DOES IT SAY "100" WHEN IT'S ONLY #2?
WHO ARE THESE PEOPLE ON THE FRONT COVER?
"BLACK CHROME AND OLEO"??
TOO ESOTERIC
TOO CONFUSING
COMPLAINTS
ON THE FLIP SIDE: I LANDED A PREVIEW IN THE PRESTIGIOUS CBG...
son is previewed
...AND ORDERS FOR HAPPY BIRTHDAY WERE ALMOST AS HIGH AS FOR DARK GNAT.
MISTER DISTRIBUTOR BIG CITY, USA
ORDER NUMBER 001101
TO: DIMENSION GRAPHICS
QUANTITY
TITLE
almost as many but not quite
Gnatrat: Early Years
Happy Birthday Gnatrat
I WAS ON A ROLL ... I WAS HOT...
AN IDEA WAS FORMING. A LITTLE BIRDIE TOLD ME...
GO FOR IT! GIVE IT ALL YA GOT!
WHILE A BUG IN MY EAR SAID...
DON'T PUT ALL YOUR EGGS IN ONE SHOE!
I MADE MY DECISION--
GET THIS BUG OUTA MY EAR!
ORKIN
THE EXTERMINATOR IS IN
©1987 MARK MARTIN
GO AHEAD AND LAUGH YOU FOOLS!
HA
HEY MARTIN GONNA DO A PARODY?
BLACK + WHITE IS DEAD MAN
YET ANOTHER COMIC PUBLISHER TO BE ERECTED HERE
MEANWHILE... SINISTER FORCES WERE AT WORK
GET TO WORK, YA BUMS! YOU'RE ON THE CLOCK!
THE STANDS WERE BECOMING A COMIC BOOK WASTELAND...
MY TURN
EASTERN STUFF
DING DONG PREVIEW
REAGAN COMICS
CAT BAT
FAT HAT
HOT
BARF!!
BARF!! THE SPECIAL EDITION
DISTRIBUTORS AND RETAILERS ACTUALLY ORDERED THE STUFF
I GOTTA ORDER THE STUFF
SUPPOSIN' SOMEBODY WANTS ONE--
--IF I DON'T GOT IT, THEY GO DOWN TO "Y" COMICS!
BESIDES IT COULD GET HOT
X COMICS
CASH FLOW PROBLEMS AND RUMORS RAN RAMPANT...
PSST... HEY BUDDY... DON'T SEND NO COMICS TO PECKERWOOD! PASS IT ON!!
+ BEHIND IT ALL (OR SO THEY SAY) -- THE DREADED COMIC GLUT!
FASTER! FASTER
GRUNT!
GASP!
TO TOP IT ALL OFF, MY BOOK WAS COMING OUT IN FEBRUARY, A HISTORICALLY 'DEAD' MONTH FOR COMICS
COMICS etc
CLOSED
CLOSED TIL SUMMER
BIG DEAL! ...SO THE INDUSTRY WAS IN TROUBLE-- SO WHAT! I HAD A QUALITY PRODUCT--
IT'S GONNA BE NEAT! TWO (2) STORIES!! COLOR COVERS! COLOR INSERT!! SAME LOW PRICE!
DARERAT
I SENT FANCY SCHMANCY SOLICITATION PACKAGES TO EVERY KNOWN DISTRIBUTOR IN THE FREE WORLD ....
For you
PERIODIC UPDATES TO SAME...
MIGHTY PUMPKIN UPDATE
VOL. XXIII NO. CXVII
I'M STILL HERE IN CASE YOU WERE WONDERING

T-SHIRTS... TIE-INS... ADS... EXTRACOMICULAR ACTIVITIES... EVERYTHING WAS RUNNING LIKE A WELL-OILED YOYO. ALL I HAD TO DO WAS FINISH THE BOOK AND WAIT FOR THOSE ORDERS TO COME ROLLING IN—
TIC TIC TIC TIC TIC
IN ALL HONESTY, I MUST CONFESS... I REALLY DROPPED THE BALL HERE
AGAIN?
IT'S HERE
AMAZING HEROES Preview Special
STARDATE - JANUARY 5: MY FIRST ORDER ARRIVES.
GIMME THAT!
MAIL
SHRIEEK
TINY ORDER
THIS COULD NOT BE TRUE!
LIAR
SUBSEQUENT ORDERS WERE EQUALLY DISMAL...
DARK GNAT
HAPPY B'DAY
DARE RAT
AND ABOUT 30% OF THESE ARE FROM ACCOUNTS WHO HAVEN'T PAID FOR HAPPY BIRTHDAY YET
BUT I NEED THE EXPOSURE
BUT I CAN'T JUST GIVE 'EM AWAY
BUT I NEED
BUT
BUT
PUFF
FRET
IT'S ALL YOUR FAULT!
KICK!
AW, @*#€&!! IT AIN'T YOUR FAULT. YOU JUST DRAW THE STUFF... THOSE DUMB DEALERS JUST BOUGHT TOO MUCH AND NOW THEY'RE OVERREACTING AND UNDERORDERING!!
JERKS! MEANIES!! I'LL SHOW THEM! I'LL DRAW A CARTOON AND EXPOSE THEIR WICKED UNDERBELLIES!!
POISON PEN
EMERGENCY USE ONLY!
WHO AM I KIDDING? NOBODY CARES ABOUT ALL THIS GARBAGE
THEY'RE RIGHT...
OH WELL
HO HUM..
WHO CARES?
GNATRAT WAS JUST A FLUKE-- PEOPLE JUST BOUGHT GNATRAT TO PAD THEIR DARK KNIGHT COLLECTIONS--
IT'S NOT THEIR PROBLEM
I'M JUST A SORE SPORT
THE DUMPS
THEN A LITTLE BIRDIE SAID...
SNAP OUT OF IT PUMPIE-- MAYBE GNATRAT WAS A FLUKE.... WELL, MAYBE THIS IS A FLUKE TOO! WHO SAID ALL YOUR FLUKES HAD TO BE GOOD, BIG SHOT?
AND YOU BETTER GET UP OFF YER CAN AND START ON YOUR NEXT BOOK, OR YOU'RE GONNA HAVTA GET A JOB!!
WHEN I COUNT TO THREE, YOU WILL FORGET EVERYTHING YOU JUST READ AND YOU WILL BELIEVE ALL I AM ABOUT TO SAY--
ONE
TWO
THREE
GNATRAT WAS HOT
GNATRAT
DARERAT IS HOTTER
POOF!
BOAT? WHAT BOAT? THIS IS MY NEW TRANS-AM!
WATCH THIS SPACE...

COMIC HIJACK

If you haven't looked at ***comic books*** *in a while,* ***shame on you***

BY LASAGNA LAGNA

It's hot as a blue pistol, and it's gnatty. In the forest, pointless redundant comics are published and trivial crimes and sins are committed like clockwork; meanwhile the world and its pampered inhabitants suffer as fossil fuels are finally used up and the industrial society collapses. Worst of all, there's never anything to watch on television except news and old Zorro movies.

A lone rat watches it all from his ivory tower. Once he was a rat with a mission—bent on revenge, a deadly vigilant force. Now he sees Art Gangs taking control, as he grows sick and nauseated on hot stale air and cheap wine. Somehow, he almost wants to wallow in the hopelessness of it all. Then, one night, he is pestered into semi-sobriety by a terrible horde from his past, and in a state of crystal-clear confusion, he knows, or he thinks he knows what he might need to do to squash punks and bring a true revival to the self-indulgent comic book industry. "It's kill or be bored to death," he thinks. That night a hurricane screams through the forest—and he is its eye.

This strangely familiar scenario is the basis of Mark Martin's work *The Dark Gnat Returns*, an unusually satiric and disturbing graphic novella that features the rebirth of comicdom's oldest and best-loved rat: a decrepit old gazillionaire named Boo Swain, better known to you as—Gnatrat. No kidding, Gnatrat.

The Dark Gnat Returns is pulp fiction in its most diluted form: a parody. If that sounds like an anticlimactic or hypocritical premise for a book of this sort, that's tough. In recent months, the comic-book industry has really been chewing its cud, and if you think you've seen the last of it, you're in for a rude awakening. Never in its fifty-year history has this business been so

Artist ***Mark Martin*** *has turned one of fandom's most cherished icons into a ninety-year-old rat.*

56

AS FEATURED IN *ROCKING ROLL* MAGAZINE

THE DARK GNAT™ RETURNS

32 B&W PAGES • COLOR COVERS • SHIPPING IN JULY

a one-shot graphic novella from prelude graphics™

Advertising art for The Dark Gnat Returns

Advertising art for Happy Birthday Gnatrat

Advertising art for Darerat/Tadpole

Advertising art for THE END featured Ramtha, the 2,000-year-old channeling goat. Ramtha does not appear in the final version (see next page).

The next 3 pages contain artwork from the original version of THE END. This artwork (and some of the other artwork in this section) was cut from the kinder, gentler version you are holding now.

CHUCK, THIS REPORT --WELLLL
FILL 'ER UP
A Bureaucratic Boondoggle by Chuck Duck
AH, YES--MY REPORT
FISHER PRICE DUCK ALONG

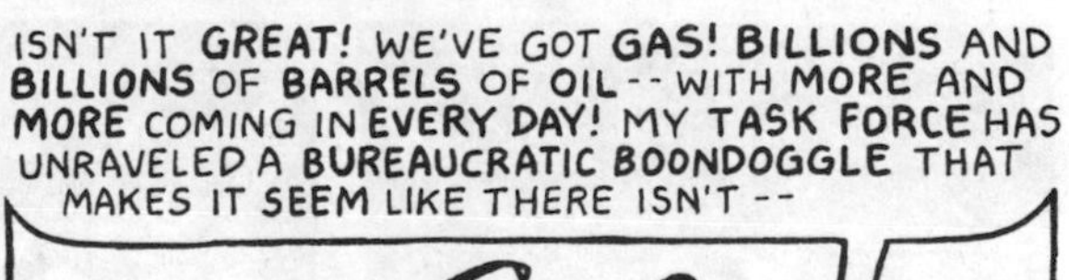
ISN'T IT GREAT! WE'VE GOT GAS! BILLIONS AND BILLIONS OF BARRELS OF OIL--WITH MORE AND MORE COMING IN EVERY DAY! MY TASK FORCE HAS UNRAVELED A BUREAUCRATIC BOONDOGGLE THAT MAKES IT SEEM LIKE THERE ISN'T --

WAK?
I CHALLENGE ANYONE TO REMEMBER EXACTLY WHAT THEY DID ON ANY GIVEN DAY, BUT I'M ALMOST KINDA SURE I TOLD YOU WHEN WE GAVE YOU THIS JOB -- YOU'RE NOT TO DO ANYTHING -- YOU'RE SUPPOSED TO MAKE EVERYBODY THINK YOU'RE DOING SOMETHING!

FIRE HIM FIRE HIM! CHECK HIS URINE!
BUT MOMSY-- HE DOESN'T--UH-- YOU KNOW--
--DO THAT--

GULP

GOOOo
PUTT!
?
?
GAS
?
?
?
?
?

THE HERO LOCKED IN STRUGGLE!

CONSTIPATED GNATRAT™

A rose
is a rose
is a good
five cent
cigar. . .
. . .but
a Thing
of Beauty
is a Joy
Forever!
MARK
MARTIN
©87
IT'S
Nebish
KRAK!
TIME!
RESERVED
FOR
BOG
MARK
MARTIN
©87

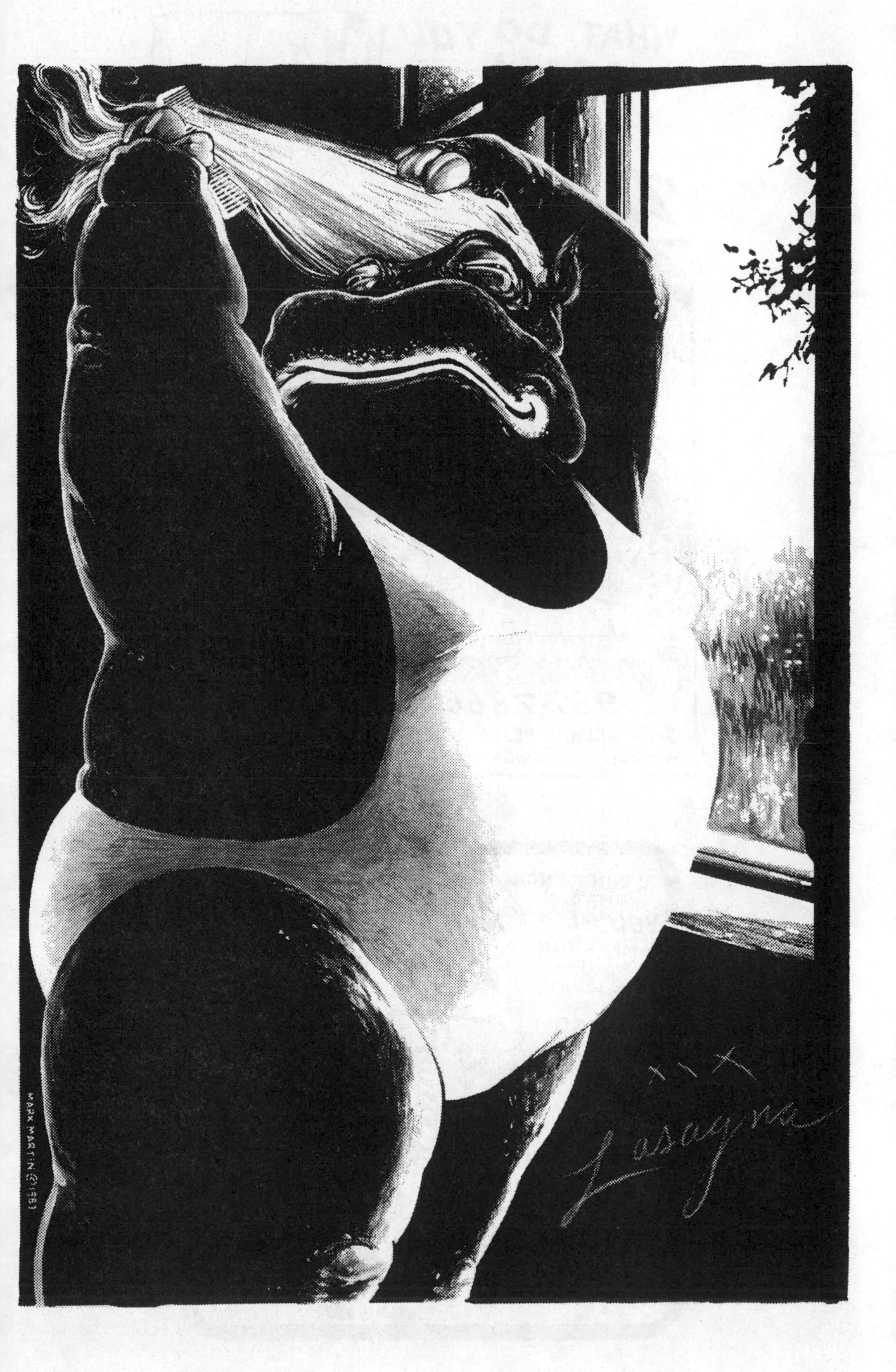

MARK MARTIN ©1983
Lasagna

WHAT DO YOU MEAN YOU NEVER HEARDA ZAMFIR ???
HE SHOULDA CALLED
WUXTRY
967-7866
3156 CAHABA HEIGHTS VILLAGE
MUSICAL RECORDINGS BOUGHT / SOLD
© TM MARK MARTIN

I DON'T KNOW WHAT YOU'RE COMPLAINING ABOUT-- LOOK WHAT ALL I'M CARRYING ON MY BACK!!
PADUCAH 600 MI.
MARK © 87

WALKER'S
COMICS
GNATRAT? YEAH, I HAD ONE AROUND HERE SOMEWHERE--
SH
EL PASO
MR. JONES
'SCUSE ME MARK
X-COW
BIG SIS
COMICS
COMICS
COMICS
COMICS
COMICS
WOW! NOW YOU CAN SIT AND FIDDLE WITH A JOYSTICK FOREVER!
CONSTANT REMINDER DEATH
CLEAN MAN
COLLECTED ADVENTURES OF MOE!
LI'L JEFFEEE
©1988 MARK MARTIN

GEEZ, WOLVIE, WHEN'S THE LAST TIME YA CUT THESE ?? UGHHN GRUNT!! THERE! CLEANLINESS IS NEXT TA GODLINESS, YA KNOW — NOW HOW BOUT A PERM FOR THOSE ARMS — HAVIN A SPECIAL THIS WEEK-...
Pretty BOO-TIQU
PERMANENTS
MANICURES
B-HINEY-WAX
WOKKA
VIDAL BABOON SHAMPU
SNIP.
GNATRAT © MARK MARTIN / WOLVERINE © MARVEL COMIX
for: THE THRILL.
from: THE PUMP.

SOLDIER!!
WHAT'S THE MEANING OF THIS ?!?
JUMPIN JIMINY WOULDJA LOOKIT THE SIZE A' THIS EGG I JUST LAID!!
SALUTE, DAMIT!
5¢
SMITH
10¢
FREE RIDE
WAH
SUM A' TH' FELLERS DON'T B'LEIVE ME THET MARK MARTIN IS MUH NATCHURL-BORND BRUTHER
SIR!
©1988 MARK "NATCHURL BORND BRUTHER OF GOMER SMITH USMC" MARTIN

The Ar-teest at work

The only time
I ever screwed up
and put the
dark lens
on the left.